PATIENT-CENTERED
STRATEGY

Other titles from

Catalysis

Inspiring Healthcare Leaders
Accelerating Change

On the Mend:
Revolutionizing Healthcare to
Save Lives and Transform the Industry
by John Toussaint, MD
and Roger A. Gerard, PhD

Potent Medicine:
The Collaborative Cure for Healthcare
by John Toussaint, MD
with Emily Adams

Management on the Mend:
The Healthcare Guide to System Transformation
by John Toussaint, MD
with Emily Adams

Beyond Heroes:
A Lean Management System for Healthcare
by Kim Barnas
with Emily Adams

Inspiring Healthcare Leaders
Accelerating Change

PATIENT-CENTERED
STRATEGY

A Learning System for
Better Care

JEFF HUNTER
with Larry Rothstein

FOREWORD BY JOHN TOUSSAINT, MD

Appleton, WI

Inspiring Healthcare Leaders
Accelerating Change

Catalysis
100 W. Lawrence Street
Appleton, WI 54911 USA
createvalue.org

Publisher's Cataloging-in-Publication Data
Hunter, Jeff.

 Patient-centered strategy : a learning system for better care /
 by Jeff Hunter with Larry Rothstein. – Appleton, WI : Catalysis, 2018.

 p. ; cm.

 ISBN13: 978-0-9848848-8-9

 1. Health services administration—United States.
 2. Medical care—United States. I. Title. II. Rothstein, Larry.

RA971.H86 2018
362.1068—dc23   2018936152

FIRST EDITION

Project coordination by Jenkins Group, Inc.
BookPublishing.com

Front cover design by Ronald Cruz, cruzialdesigns.com
Interior layout by Yvonne Fetig Roehler

Printed in the United States of America

22   21   20   19   18   •   5   4   3   2   1

To my parents, Nan and Bill Hunter.

I never thanked you enough.

Contents

Foreword

Traditional healthcare delivery in the United States is eroding rapidly. The push for value rather than volume is upending the "heads in beds" strategic thinking of hospital leaders. Start-ups—such as freestanding imaging centers—that once nibbled at the edges of profitable services now are taking big bites. Insurers are entering the physician practice business and integrating financing and delivery. Technology is enabling new care processes that are cannibalizing inpatient hospital services. Optum, a division of United Healthcare and the largest commercial insurer in America, now employs more than 30,000 healthcare providers. Amazon, Berkshire Hathaway, and JPMorgan Chase have recently announced that they are entering the game with the goal to provide simplified, high-quality healthcare for their employees at a reasonable cost. Free from profit-making incentives and constraints, these organizations admit they have few answers but believe joining together to improve healthcare cost and quality is a good use of their immense resources.

Designing care closer to the patient is already occurring. Technology is enabling new care processes that are eroding inpatient hospital services. The "Hospital at Home" model, originally developed by Johns Hopkins Hospital researchers and aggressively applied by Mount Sinai Hospital in New York City, is emerging in many markets. The U.S. military's ability to place a state-of-the-art surgical theater anywhere in the world in fewer than 24 hours opens up the possibility of imagining how to take care of sick, elderly patients in their homes. Daily, the need for big, expensive hospitals dwindles.

Given this bleak outlook, hospital leaders must transform their business model. In this book, Jeff Hunter describes with expert precision how leaders can shed traditional strategic planning practices to create a patient-focused strategy system. The transformation starts with leaders adopting new mental models and behaving differently. They must create systems that facilitate rapid feedback from frontline caregivers, that quickly recognize environmental shifts, and that identify the unmet needs of patients. To build such a system, leaders need to change dramatically. Instead of traditional command-and-control strategic thinking, they must have regular conversations with professionals and staff—the people doing the real value-added work. That means getting to the front line and carefully listening to what caregivers and patients are telling them. As feedback rolls in, small and rapid experiments of change must be conducted. Next, these learnings must be shared broadly and spread throughout the organization. And then new experiments must be designed based on the learnings from the previous experiments.

Incorporating all this information and new behavior into an achievable ideal state is a major challenge. This new ideal state is a detailed vision of the future that is designed to deliver a much higher-quality and lower-cost patient experience. It requires radically different care processes that are planned around patients, not doctors or nurses. Most current strategy work is done in a vacuum, with little information gathered about the needs of patients. Strategy is usually based on the CEO's and board members' intuition, not grounded in facts. This must change. The era of the great strategist riding in on a white horse and supplying everyone with the answers is over. Healthcare is too complex, and there are too many variables for the hero approach to work anymore. That is why a strategic management system that is dynamic and based on what Jeff describes as lean learning loops is essential. Lean learning loops are nothing more than rapid plan-do-study-act (PDSA) cycles, with the emphasis on rapid. This involves many experiments happening simultaneously, which produces, in turn, answers that quickly drive better patient experiences and improved patient care.

Jeff lays out in this book a process of *patient-centered* strategy. This strategic management system has been tested in industries from manufacturing to the military and is reproducible in the healthcare domain. He provides detailed healthcare and non-healthcare examples that clearly show how the various components of this system interrelate. By the end of the book, you will be fully equipped to design a much more powerful system of strategy development for your healthcare organization.

The strategic management system Jeff explains is a subsystem of a broader management system known as lean thinking.

Before you exclaim, "Not another lean healthcare book!" think about what it takes to build excellence into your organization. In my experience working with hundreds of healthcare organizations, excellence is driven from the top and always involves establishing bedrock core principles of how the organization should function. From principles come the behaviors to which leaders hold themselves and others accountable. From principles and behaviors are derived the systems that support excellence.

Using lean tools makes sense only after such a foundation is laid first. Jeff explains his own mistakes and misconceptions about lean thinking throughout his personal journey. He learned, as did I, that lean thinking is not a project; it's a philosophy of management that incorporates strategy, daily management, leadership behaviors, and the radical redesign of operational processes using what are called model cells. Healthcare leaders cannot delegate their responsibility of a lean transformation to the improvement office. Lean transformation is hard. Leaders, like everyone, resist change. "Change is great as long as I don't have to do it" is the unspoken reality, unfortunately. But organizations don't transform until the leaders do. Hundreds of health systems across the globe that have undergone lean transformation stand as testimony to how adapting this approach leads to great results.

Examples abound. St. Mary's in Kitchener, Ontario, has been one of the top three hospitals in patient safety in all of Canada for three years in a row. In England, Western Sussex Hospitals NHS Foundation Trust, which runs Worthing Hospital, Southlands Hospital in Shoreham-by-Sea, and St. Richard's Hospital in Chichester, West Sussex, is one of only three trusts in the National Health Service to receive the country's top-quality award. In Johannesburg, South Africa, Charlotte Maxeke, a public hospital caring for the poor, accomplished an 80% reduction in neonatal infection rates. And at UMass Memorial Health Care in Worcester, Massachusetts, a $100-million turnaround was realized while the organization simultaneously achieved top statewide scores for cardiac care. These remarkable results can be traced to leaders embracing lean thinking and transforming themselves and then their organizations.

Jeff's book is a wake-up call to healthcare leaders that the macro-environment has changed and that traditional ways of acting are not going to work anymore. Without building a strategic management system, you can't skate to where the puck is going to be. The system Jeff describes so ably is patient focused, with a reliance on information from the people doing the real work. Strategy won't be created once a year in the boardroom. It will be created every day, studied and adjusted, and, by the next day, changed again. Why? As the buggy whip industry found with the introduction of the automobile, survival is not mandatory.

—John Toussaint, MD

Introduction

I t was one of those moments that happen in life, a moment when something you strongly believe in is upended instantly.

Sometimes this happens when a comment by your spouse or your children or a friend pierces your heart to reveal a truth; sometimes this happens when you are in high school or in college and your strongly held viewpoint is overturned by a teacher's insightful remarks.

This particular moment for me occurred in the office of my boss, John Toussaint, MD, during a performance review in the late spring of 2006.

The meeting took place at ThedaCare's corporate office in Appleton, Wisconsin, in a recently renovated building that had once housed a department store. As we spoke, ThedaCare had in fewer than 20 years grown to become the largest health system and employer in northeast Wisconsin. In 1987, two community hospitals, Appleton Medical Center and Theda Clark Medical Center, merged to form Novus Health Group. Theda Clark Medical Center had been named after a young woman who died in childbirth. James Clark, her father and one of the original founders of Kimberly-Clark, believed she would have survived if a hospital had been available to his daughter. The Clark family led the development of modern health services in northeast Wisconsin, and their name became synonymous with quality healthcare throughout the state.

The merger evolved over time into a fully integrated system with hospitals, physicians, home health, behavioral health, and a large health insurance plan. In August 1999, it changed its name to ThedaCare.

John Toussaint began practicing internal medicine in Appleton in 1985 and quickly became involved in healthcare management and improvement. For 10 years he served as ThedaCare's chief medical officer, responsible for improving the effectiveness of the care delivery system. John became ThedaCare's CEO in 2000.

Before coming to ThedaCare, I had worked in both strategy and operations for a large health system, including two stints as the CEO of community hospitals it managed. I then spent several years managing the strategy consulting practice for a hospital management company.

I joined Novus Health Group (later ThedaCare) in 1991 and spent the first decade helping ThedaCare grow the system, acquire provider groups and organizations, market its services, and develop strategic plans, as well as assisting CEOs in a variety of ways, especially with the board of trustees. By the spring day of the performance review, I had worked in healthcare for nearly 30 years.

I found strategy fascinating. I strove to be the best strategic planner I could be: I continuously read the professional literature, attended events that focused on strategic thinking, and visited other organizations to examine their strategic approaches. I had in-depth conversations about strategy with our board members and talked with renowned strategic thinkers and practitioners. I prided myself on practicing strategic techniques most would consider state-of-the-art.

When I joined ThedaCare, the then-CEO, Jim Raney, and the board of trustees made it clear that we were not going to have an outside consulting company "do our strategic plan." Developing the organization's strategy and making choices were the responsibilities of senior leadership, along with board involvement and approval. We could gain insights from outside experts, but formulating and executing strategy was our job, and we would be held accountable for what we did.

During this period, I had a clear sense of my role. In strategic planning, I was good at analyzing and synthesizing complex information about the organization's market position, and I could communicate our strategy in clear, understandable, and actionable terms. And like all the other senior leaders, when problems arose in any of the departments I was managing, I was supposed to help solve them for my direct reports. In short, I saw myself and was seen by others as an organizational hero. Whoever solved the most problems, or the biggest problems, was the biggest hero.

But as John would explain to me at the performance review, he had other thoughts about what I should be doing.

John and I had a complicated relationship. Until he became CEO, he had been my personal physician. When he took over running ThedaCare, I found myself clashing with him on various issues. John's executive style at that time could be described as "command and control." He reminded me of the character Nathan Arizona in the

Coen brothers' comedy *Raising Arizona*. When asked by a policeman whether his employees were disgruntled, Nathan replied, "They're all disgruntled ... My motto is 'Do it my way or watch your butt.'"

Like Nathan Arizona's, John's comments could be sharp and direct, and most senior leaders avoided confronting him. That was not my approach. I knew John respected my candor and my analytical mind. After all, his approach to solving problems was like mine; as an internist by training, he gathered facts to understand a patient's situation, tried interventions, studied the results, and adjusted. We worked together effectively for a decade as ThedaCare grew into a large and respected healthcare system.

John's passion was improving the consistency and quality of medical care at both the local and national levels. Based on his own experiences, he believed high levels of quality in healthcare could be achieved only by creating a sustainable system, not by individual heroics. As chief medical officer, he introduced improvement systems such as 90-day workouts, Six Sigma, and other systems. Although each one produced results, performance would always return to baseline over time.

His search continued when he became CEO. In 2003, John joined a group of local CEOs who assembled regularly to learn from one another. At one gathering, he met Dan Ariens, CEO of Ariens Company from nearby Brillion, Wisconsin. A family-owned business since 1933, Ariens specialized in tools for snow removal and lawn maintenance. After almost going bankrupt, the company had turned itself around by using lean principles, systems, and tools. George Koenigsaecker, the former president of Jacobs Manufacturing, a Danaher company, a member of the Ariens board, and a nationally respected leader of lean thinking, coached them on the initiative.

As John began to explore lean, he increasingly came to believe it might help ThedaCare achieve the lofty quality and cost improvements he had targeted. Soon after, I and other ThedaCare leaders attended an all-day session at Ariens to watch lean in action. Then we participated in a three-day retreat led by two consultants associated with Koenigsaecker. This was the beginning of our lean journey. We didn't know what we didn't know, but John loved to experiment with new ideas, and I willingly went along for the ride.

As I had with John's earlier transformational efforts, I helped him prepare for board meetings where he gave updates on our progress with lean. I integrated lean into our strategic plan and described it in glowing terms. I accompanied John when he talked about lean at new-employee orientation sessions and at management training gatherings. I even substituted for John on several occasions and endorsed the ThedaCare experience with lean.

In my mind, I believed I was supportive of John's initiative. But I didn't think lean had anything to do with strategy and marketing. I thought lean would impact operations and clinical quality, and I trusted my colleagues in those areas to implement its concepts.

So at my performance review in 2006, I was not expecting any negative comments about my participation in lean. From past reviews, I knew my superiors and my peers liked my analytical skills and my ability to translate complex concepts, find insights, and then convey them effectively. What criticism I had received was confined to my management and development of the marketing team.

John had a modest office filled with pictures of his family and of his achievements as a fly fisherman. He always held performance reviews at a small conference table. After we both sat down, John glanced at his notes on a sheet of paper, stared directly into my eyes, and opened with the same question from previous reviews: "How do you think you are doing?"

I replied as I usually did by ticking off my efforts that were going well and then talking about the things that needed to be improved. I made no mention of lean.

When I finished, John said softly, "I think you are missing the point about lean. I don't see you going on a consistent basis to the Friday report-outs. I don't think you see the connection to strategic planning."

John was right. I had skipped most of them. The Central Improvement Office had initiated Friday morning report-outs by frontline staff. At these sessions, as many as 20 people—doctors, nurses, x-ray techs, and housekeepers—discussed the impact of what were called Rapid Improvement Events throughout the healthcare system. These events were weeklong activities during which multidisciplinary frontline teams worked on difficult problems. They would report out their solutions on Fridays. The report-out was a powerful statement that management supported frontline teams in solving problems. It was important for senior management to be there. From 50 to 80 people normally attended these report-outs, which were filled with excitement and energy.

I usually didn't attend since Friday mornings were when I normally caught up with my work.

John told me that he realized that lean was a very different paradigm from traditional management approaches. He said that lean required an entire organization to think and behave differently and to become patient centered. Lean was causing him to rethink how he acted as

CEO; senior leaders like myself also had to confront our conceptions of what it is to be an executive. He added that he wanted me to fully join him in this effort as I had with other initiatives in the past. If I could see the possibilities of lean, then I could help other senior leaders to do the same. The challenging assignment he asked me to undertake was to help the senior leadership team apply lean thinking to how they, as a team, accomplished their work. And that included me and my work.

John's approach to me was different from past reviews. He wasn't Nathan Arizona any longer. He was more open and more vulnerable. He wasn't ordering me to participate in lean; he was allowing me to come to this decision myself based on my own self-reflection.

That night I pondered what to do. Did I want to rethink my entire approach to strategy? Was everything I learned and believed in wrong?

I had options. I could go to another healthcare system that preferred the historic way of planning. Or I could go back into consulting, producing strategic plans for other organizations.

The more I thought about what John had said, the more curious I became about understanding lean. Could it actually be the management system we had searched for to create excellence and the best possible patient experience? At some of the few report-outs that I had attended, I had heard about several clinical breakthroughs made by frontline staff involved in patient care every day, such as a significant reduction in door-to-balloon time and improvements in how the health system managed depression in patients. This was very profound and meaningful to me.

I had entered healthcare to make a difference.

I initially was attracted to the field while in college when I visited my grandfather in the nursing home where he spent his final days. Based on what I saw, I decided to volunteer as a recreation aide at a local nursing home run by nuns. I found myself creating activities for the few male residents, like organizing trips to see Detroit Tigers games. Such experiences led me to healthcare. At the time John and I were talking, I was once again deeply involved in a personal way with the healthcare system—my father was ill with cancer and my mother with diabetes. The reports-outs showed me it was possible to make radical improvements in care delivery, which would be important for ThedaCare and for helping patients.

I always liked being a student. John knew that. Our conversation had finally unlocked my desire to learn about this mysterious new management system.

The next day I started on my lean journey.

I began to attend the report-outs. I read books on the topic. I sought out colleagues at ThedaCare, including John Poole, senior vice president for ThedaCare Improvement System; Mike Speer, senior vice president of human resources; and Barbara Coniff of the Central Improvement Office.

When John asked me to help him apply lean to how a senior leadership team creates value in their work, I called Barbara. She gave me a book by lean experts John Shook and Mike Rother entitled *Learning to See*. I felt embarrassed because the senior leadership team was assigned the book a year earlier; I had given it a quick scan then, but I hadn't seen any relevance to my work and put it aside. I carefully read it this time.

I continued my journey for years. I sought advice from experts on the topic and insights from practitioners in a variety of organizations including healthcare, businesses, and nonprofits.

Finally, as I began to learn how to help my direct reports apply lean thinking, the real meaning of the concept crystallized: my role was not to be the best possible strategic planner; rather, my task was to build the organization's strategic planning *capability*. For any of the other functions that I managed, my role was to help my direct reports build organizational capability. In short, I had to develop ThedaCare's people to solve problems and improve our processes to better serve our purpose.

As my journey expanded beyond ThedaCare, I discovered four recurring problems that healthcare leaders encountered. They suffered from overburden (avoiding strategic choices), imitation (not having meaningful differentiation from their competitors), inertia (caused by not having rapid learning cycles), and confusion (the result of ineffective alignment of strategic intent with the frontline staff). Confusion is the result of no strategy deployment. Strategy deployment, also referred to as *hoshin kanri*, is the process of creating and cascading strategic intent throughout an organization so everyone from the board to frontline workers clearly understands what is most important and what his or her role is in achieving a strategy.

This book's purpose is to describe the strategic management subsystem that fits within the broader lean management system. This subsystem includes the principles that are the universal truths from which the system is derived: the leadership behaviors that are guided by the principles and the processes and tools that are required for creating and managing strategy. This system will be introduced in the following 10 chapters. Chapter 1, "A Personal Awakening," is about replacing an old, ineffective system, and the mental model upon which it's based, with more relevant principles, systems, and tools. Chapter 2, "Putting Strategy back in Strategy Deployment," is about choosing the critical few initiatives that will create lasting value for customers. Chapters 3 through 8 describe the elements of the new system for formulating and deploying strategy: chapter 3, "Understanding the Mess"; chapter 4, "Framing the Strategic Issue"; chapter 5, "Making Strategic Choices to Close the Gap"; chapter 6, "Strategy Deployment through Rapid Experimentation"; chapter 7, "The Technical and Human Sides of Catch-Ball"; and chapter 8, "Managing Focus and Accelerating Learning." Chapter 9, "A Subset of a Larger System," shows how this strategic management system fits within the larger lean management system, and chapter 10, "The Journey Ahead," is a summary of the lessons learned and the path forward for readers.

Your journey will not be easy. Mine has not been. The path is not linear, and I frequently had to backtrack. Lean takes time and energy, and there is enormous inertia to overcome. Healthcare systems are also very complex, and, currently, no one organization has completely centered its strategies on patients. But I have experienced enough success to believe it can be done.

I don't know exactly how far I have come on this journey, although it is a significant way. I do know there are more miles to go. I am forever grateful to John Toussaint and many others for starting me on this incredible adventure. My belief is that you will be also.

Chapter 1

A Personal
Awakening

We don't need another hero.
—Tina Turner
Mad Max Beyond Thunderdome

We all have our heroes, and most of us aspire to be heroic at some point in our lives. For me, it first occurred when I was a sophomore in high school in Franklinville, New York. My team made it to the regional basketball championship game, and I came off the bench, despite a heavily bandaged knee, to score nine points in the first quarter. At the end of the game, I grabbed three straight rebounds to help seal the victory for us.

The next day my exploits were mentioned in the *Buffalo News*, and a few hours later my dad and I heard the article being read, in its entirety, over the local radio station by sportscaster and former Buffalo Bills great Ernie Warlick.

"Glory days," as Bruce Springsteen would say.

But these days were not confined to childhood, as the Boss's song describes. I spent most of my professional life thinking I was still a hero. Heroic action is what our culture teaches us to replicate in our lives if possible. Luke Skywalker, Tom Brady, Rosa Parks, Wonder Woman, Neil Armstrong—heroes all, whether real or fictional. We all want to defeat Darth Vader, or throw the winning touchdown at the Super Bowl, or ignite a revolution in civil rights, or defeat Nazis, or be the first to walk on the moon. But such noble aims can be destructive within the context of an organization, particularly if they help form a mental model that inhibits innovation and change.

I wasn't consciously aware of what MIT's Peter Senge would call my "mental model" until I began my lean journey. In his groundbreaking book *The Fifth Discipline: The Art and Practice of the Learning Organization,* Senge defined a mental model as "deeply held internal images of how the world works, images that limit us to familiar ways of thinking and acting. Very often, we are not consciously aware of our mental models or the effects they have on our behavior."

It may seem incongruous to equate heroic aspirations with the activities of a strategic planner, but I definitely fit the description found in Kim Barnas's book *Beyond Heroes.* In fact, I believe almost all strategic planning other than lean is undergirded by a belief in heroes. My story, far from being unique, has been the norm for decades.

I got my initial hero training in the 1980s from Bill Katz, one of the country's best strategic planning experts, from the renowned consulting firm of Arthur D. Little. Bill was a wonderful human being and a great teacher. He showed me how to diagnose a healthcare system's market position and to find solutions to problems by analyzing data from in-depth marketing research. The strategic plans he showed me were loaded with statistical analysis and charts.

Bill's teachings built on the management ideas of the time. Strategic plans would be designed by the smartest leaders, who would diagnose problems or opportunities, develop solutions, and then issue orders to be carried out. If the plans didn't work, it must have been a problem with faulty execution by someone else down the line.

Armed with Bill's approach, I became a practitioner. From 1987 to 1991 I constructed strategic plans for the client hospitals of Brim Healthcare.

My strategic plans, like the ones I still see at hospitals, were big and broad—all things to all people in a defined geographic area. The plan would coexist with other large initiatives and contain three- to five-year time lines with an annual upgrade. These plans usually involved buying new technology, recruiting new personnel, and constructing new buildings. Initiatives also included developing better safety methods, improving quality, increasing customer satisfaction, engaging employees to increase morale, and spurring financial performance. The resources to execute these efforts took the form of annual operating plans and budgets.

Under the strategies I and other planners constructed, CEOs avoided making choices—which was fine with them. Establishing priorities and saying no to others might upset key stakeholders such as doctors, managers, boards of directors, donors, community groups, and accreditation agencies. Many CEOs secretly expected that managers below the C-suite would make the resource allocation decisions. Regrettably, those managers lacked the power and the resources to assume that responsibility.

By not making choices, however, these organizations did not differentiate themselves with initiatives that would create unique, relevant value for patients, which ultimately created a commodity market. When all competitors pursue essentially the same strategic intent with similar initiatives and obtain identical results, patients cannot discern a difference among them and therefore make decisions based exclusively on price.

But since all consultants, including myself, essentially created the same strategic plans for hospitals, we could do no wrong. Our lack of innovation had few consequences since the growing demand for hospitals and doctor services led to ever greater revenue, despite the lack of differentiation between them.

When I joined ThedaCare in 1991 as the senior vice president of strategy and marketing, my responsibility was to write a plan for board approval. With the CEO, I organized the annual strategic planning retreats that included board members and, eventually, medical staff leadership. My task, however, was the same as when I was a consultant—produce a large document that would outline what the organization would be doing for the next three to five years. Input on the plan would come from the CEO, the senior leadership, groups of physicians, a strategic planning committee, and several members of the board. I would present the plan at the annual board retreat. After the plan was approved by the board, it would be refreshed annually, and it would be communicated through an intranet posting and printed out for anyone who wanted to read it. There were never a lot of takers.

In retrospect, I can now see that there were actually two problems. First was its hero orientation: the plan was basically a description of what each of the heroes at ThedaCare was doing in the organization. The second was that the plan was expected to make everybody happy. It was to include every idea of what anybody thought he or she should or could be doing for the next three to five years. That generated a Christmas list of possibilities, which were then grouped into five or so categories. By not making choices, to avoid conflict, we were dumbing down the plan to its least common denominator.

Just as I had been as a consultant, I was not responsible for the plan's implementation. That task was left to senior leaders in operations. If I had bothered to ask, I would have found a common response from managers about my plans—they were too busy to do anything about them. A disconnect existed between formulating the plan and establishing its deployment, but it didn't seem to matter.

Over time in my lean journey I learned why this happened: the old leadership model conceived of organizations as biologic beings. In this metaphor, an executive leadership team is like a person's brain. The brain predetermines what is going to happen and sends out signals to the staff, who do exactly what they are told. Customers and competitors also behave exactly as expected. The strategic planner's job is to capture the senior leadership's collective thoughts and send out directions to subordinates.

Strategic plans developed in this manner begin to deteriorate the day after the document is produced. They are based on faulty assumptions about patient adoption, competitor response, organizational capabilities, and industry structure. If you believe in systems thinking, you cannot predict or predetermine (control) everything that is going to happen, no matter how much market intelligence you have. Once you take action—begin to implement your strategy—you change the game. You influence the world around you. Your action generates multiple reactions, only some of which you can anticipate.

ThedaCare, however, did not suffer during the 1990s because of the inadequacies of the planning process. Money poured in from Medicare, Medicaid, and private insurance companies. Soaring costs were passed on to customers. ThedaCare owned a health plan in partnership with independent physicians. The organization grew by selling its healthcare insurance plan to employers and by increasing member enrollment. By the late 1990s, we were the largest hospital system in northeast Wisconsin. During this time, I received lots of positive feedback from the board and from our CEO for the strategic plans and the processes I was putting together.

When John Toussaint became CEO in 2000, the board of trustees challenged us to project our strategic thinking much further into the future. The board members felt our plans were starting to look the same year after year, and, based on assumptions about ourselves, our customers, and our competitors, that might not be true forever.

They were right. The sources of competitive advantage we had enjoyed in the 1990s were eroding rapidly. By the early 2000s, numerous media reports attacked HMOs for restricting patients' access to specialists and various kinds of treatments, causing a decline in enrollment. In addition, our health insurance company—a gatekeeper model health maintenance organization (HMO) that we sold to local employers— could no longer drive our growth. International conglomerates had bought out a number of local area companies. These conglomerates were looking for national healthcare networks that could cover their employees' health insurance needs. We had to think more broadly, and we had to fundamentally question our strategy. We were spending all of our leadership time trying to manage insurance risk, geographically grow the health plan by contracting with our competitors, and adding the new technological capabilities required to stay in the insurance company game.

The real story here is that we had to fundamentally question our business model because the situation had changed. Many people in our organization were deeply committed to our business model of insuring lives and then taking care of their medical needs. We were an insurance-first business model. Senior leaders were considering that we should change our model to focus on care delivery. After three years of internal debate, we finally resolved the debate by selling the health plan and focusing on care delivery.

As the strategist supporting this decision process, I could not rely on my old skills of analyzing the market and convincing people that I had the solution. I needed to learn how to facilitate other people's thinking.

Although John and I were both in the early stages of learning about lean, we recognized that our mental models were antiquated and that any effort would involve the active participation of the senior leadership. We decided to experiment with scenario planning, which we had first learned about in the 1990s. Simply put, scenario planning is a structured way for organizations to think about the future. Stakeholders from inside and outside the organization meet and develop a small number of scenarios—stories about how the future might unfold and how this might affect the industry and, ultimately, their organization. The stories help executives recognize and adapt to changing environments.

In fact, Arie de Geus, the former head of planning for Royal Dutch Shell, used scenario planning extensively, and it helped Shell jump from the seventh-largest oil company to second place during the industry turbulence of the 1970s. In a 1988 article for the *Harvard Business Review*, de Geus defined the core difference between traditional planning and scenario planning: "Planning means changing minds, not making plans." He added, "We think of planning as learning, and corporate planning as institutional learning."

By this time in my journey, I had begun to see that it was important to expand the group who thought about strategy and that my role was to facilitate such discussions. However, the cracks were very small in my mental model. In retrospect, I can see that I was still acting like a hero, except now I was a hero facilitator.

More cracks happened after I began to internalize some of the lean concepts that had been introduced at ThedaCare.

My first serious departure from my mental model occurred in 2006 when John asked me to join him on the lean journey by helping our senior leadership team understand the process by which it created value for patients and communities. This began with facilitating the senior leadership team to discover and develop work functions in six domains of value-creating processes: strategy formulation, strategy deployment, resource allocation, monitoring performance, cultural development, and key relationships. For the first time as a group we could define in each of these domains what actions we took that created value and, just as important, what actions that did not create value. This was the senior team's first foray into developing standard work. Standard work is a documented process for achieving a task. Without an agreed-upon standard approach, work cannot be improved. A notion of what work was existed in our minds, but each executive had his or her own opinion, and everyone's opinion was different. With the development of the standard work for the six domains, we were all finally singing from the same song sheet.

A further breakthrough occurred in 2009 when Dean Gruner asked me to help him improve the value of our senior leadership by experimenting with how we spent time in meetings. By this point, Dean had become CEO of ThedaCare, with John Toussaint leaving to head up the ThedaCare Center for Healthcare Value, which later became Catalysis. Dean had followed John as chief medical officer at ThedaCare and was also a firm believer in the benefits of lean.

In this period, senior leaders were spending a lot of time in meetings, including two senior leader meetings a week. At the first meeting they were to discuss capital allocation and finance. At the second meeting they were required to devote three hours to strategy. But the meetings quickly devolved into a hodge-podge of operational issues mixed in with strategic discussions. In addition to these meetings, every quarter they would have a two-day retreat to discuss strategy.

The question Dean raised was: Are they using meeting time correctly? The answer could be found only by asking more questions within a lean framework: Are they creating value for patients at these meetings? Are they spending too much time on the meetings? What should they be doing at these meetings?

Instead of trying to figure this out by myself, I followed plan-do-study-adjust thinking and facilitated the process with senior leaders. I conducted a small survey of the 10 senior leaders who attended these meetings. I looked at the six dimensions of senior leadership work we had developed. I found agreement on how much time we were spending on meetings but little agreement on how much time we *should be* spending and on what topics.

Based on the survey, we talked through how to better use our time in meetings to create value. Eventually, a consensus was reached that we should spend more time on strategy formulation and deployment and less time on monitoring organizational performance and resource allocation. This did not mean that we would not be accountable for the results in these areas; it meant that we would find a more effective and efficient process by which we created value in these domains.

For example, we redesigned the process by which we would manage resource allocation. We decided that the senior leadership team would set annual parameters and priorities for capital projects. During the rest of the year, the Capital Allocation Review Team, which engaged more leaders in the organization, would make actual decisions on which projects to fund. We also redesigned the process for monitoring performance. And we engaged more leaders throughout the organization in bimonthly reviews in addition to our own senior leadership review every week. The result was that more and more people were acquiring a sense of how the organization was performing. When we remeasured the percentage of the time we spent in each of the domains, we found that our time spent was closer to where we thought it should be spent. We also found that our results had improved in each of those domains.

Another significant advance in my lean thinking happened in 2011 after I received feedback from senior leaders that they thought not enough people were involved in putting together the strategic plan. This was initially frustrating to me because I believed they were questioning my capability as a strategic planning hero. However, I quickly realized they were asking whether the process could become better if we were to include more people in a more meaningful manner. I again researched best practices, and I used the principles, systems, and tools of lean thinking to engage all key stakeholders in a reinvention of the strategic planning value stream. A value stream is the sequenced set of steps and information flow that is required to deliver a specific product or service to the customer.

At the beginning of the redesigned process, we conducted a written external and internal market position assessment in the first quarter of every year. Then we shared it throughout the organization, including with frontline workers, to obtain feedback. After that, we brought it in June to the board of trustees for their reaction. Then we developed breakthrough initiatives (action plans) and updated the written strategic plan for the board's approval in August. Each year, we improved this value stream, making it better, faster, and cheaper. Each year, we tried further improvements to involve more information from the front lines that would be fed back into the strategic planning process. This value stream was a significant step in building an organizational capacity and a shared process around strategy for ThedaCare.

Another major crack in my mental model occurred in 2013 when senior leadership team members disagreed, once again, about the fundamental business model. That was, of course, the year that the Affordable Care Act, or Obamacare, began to be implemented. Consumer exchanges opened, and employer mandates were enacted. The healthcare world was turned upside down.

We began a debate that lasted for a year about who was our customer. Was it the patient? Or was it the payer? Should our business model be patient centric or payer centric? Some senior leaders felt that we had to get back into the insurance business that we had abandoned in 2003.

I explored a number of best practices, particularly the work of Lafley and Martin, Tim Brown, Matthew May, Eric Ries, and Steve Blank.

I began to see a connection between design thinking, lean start-up, and customer development. Out of this work would come the system of strategy formation and strategy deployment that forms the core of this book.

Innovators in fast-moving industries use "design thinking" principles and methods to create unique value for customers and to surprise and surpass competitors—the essence of strategic planning. Tim Brown, the CEO of IDEO, an international design and consulting firm, defines design thinking as "a discipline using the designer's sensibility and methods to match people's needs with what is conceptually feasible and what a viable strategy can convert into value and opportunity."

Brown's thinking is paralleled by strategy and innovation advisor Matthew May's strategic innovation system. May helped me see that there are three intersecting "gears" of design and strategy. He calls them humanizing, conceptualizing, and strategizing. Humanizing involves uncovering a customer's latent and emergent needs through ethnographic approaches to research such as interviewing and directly observing. Conceptualizing starts with a minimum viable product, the most basic form of value proposition intended to solve the customer's need. Those in the organization conducting the experiments continue to build out the solution by using lean learning loops—iterations of experiments that expand the solution by adding features that create value for customers and discarding features that don't. Strategizing consists of scaling the solution into a financially sustainable business model.

Silicon Valley entrepreneur and Stanford University Professor Steve Blank, in his book *The Four Steps to the Epiphany*, coined the term "customer development." This describes his innovative four-step approach to creating solutions for customers by observing how customers interact with experiments so their issues and pain points can be discerned and solved. Then the solution is scaled and taken to market. In *The Lean Startup,* entrepreneur Eric Ries expanded on the notion of customer development by rapidly building out solutions using what he calls build-measure-learn feedback loops. Starting with a minimum viable product, through a disciplined process of rapid experimentation, strategists use lean learning loops to pivot or persevere until the solution is ready for market.

As I studied these various approaches, I realized they are not different from each other; they build on each other, forming a new mental model for strategic management. The convergence of customer development, design thinking, and lean startup with strategy results in a paradigm where:

- Deep customer insights are continually gathered.

- Strategic options are generated, choices are made, and hypotheses are formed.

- Rapid experimentation begins on the most critical and unknown assumptions with a minimum viable product and builds a solution in the fastest and most cost-effective manner.

This is similar to the PDSA thinking of lean. When you choose a strategy, you are defining a hypothetical solution to close a gap, based on your perceived understanding of the situation. You are making assumptions about the intentions and behaviors of others. Fueled by deep customer insights, you start with a minimum viable product and build out your solution through rapid experimentation using lean learning loops.

This is how clinicians on the front line solve problems and improve the process by which they create value for patients. They grasp the situation, formulate a plan, try experiments, study the results, and adjust—pivoting or persevering, depending on what they are observing.

This way of strategizing becomes nested in the organization, and it can radically change the way individuals think. It happened to me. At this point in my lean journey, my old mental model was completely shattered. I realized that I had experienced a breakthrough moment when I received a call from a rural hospital CEO in the ThedaCare System.

The CEO explained his hypothesis that starting a transportation service would increase value to patients. He believed that patients in a nearby community were not coming to his hospital because they lacked transportation. He asked what I thought about buying a van, refurbishing it, hiring a driver, and then marketing a new transportation service. That would cost the hospital about $100,000. The Jeff who operated under the old strategic planning framework would have said, "Let's do some market research [which would take three months], then write the business plan and send it through the approval cycle [which will take another four months]. In six to nine months you might get approval for the $100,000." Instead, I said, "I don't know; it could be a good idea. What must be true for that transportation service to work the way you expect?" After talking, we agreed that his riskiest assumption was whether people would use the van. I asked him whether there was a low-risk way to test that assumption. He said, "Yes, there is a local service I could rent on a per-use basis." He experimented with this minimum viable product and found that transportation wasn't the problem. For almost no money and little time, he pivoted onto his next hypothesis.

I began to apply my new mental model to the other value streams for which I was accountable, starting with marketing and then moving to philanthropy. As I did, I saw further evidence that this way of leading was far superior because I was helping people and teams develop their problem-solving capabilities. Initially, it was emotionally very difficult for me. I was used to people coming to my office with problems and I would solve them. Even as I progressed with lean and I was shifting into being more of a coach, I still wanted them to come to my office. I soon realized that this was not completely effective. I had to leave my lair and my trappings of authority and go to where people were creating value. That is where the work is done each day.

When I did this, I could see how the individuals were practicing leader standard work. We've discussed how standard work for the senior team helped everyone to be aligned. A leader's standard work is the work processes that guide the individual leader's day. It's quite specific to each leader, and it is the way by which each leader knows he or she is focused on the right work. It starts with managing one's calendar. The leader's standard work is focused on the reproducible activities that will add value to customers. It needs to be visual, usually up on a wall in an office, and it outlines what the leader is supposed to be doing each day. Once this standard work was in place, it helped me greatly to coach my team and help them in their development.

I was finally seeing the potential of lean to engage employees at all levels in the organization in the process of creating new value for customers. Frontline caregivers are in a position to observe the pain points of customers and to figure out innovative ways to solve them.

My old mental model was top-down, senior management as brain, me as hero analyst and communicator. Instead, my new mental model was organization as social system, with me as coach and facilitator developing capability in others and strategic planning as a nimble process of organizational learning. PDSA is the common language that binds us; PDSA is how we get to a patient-centered strategy.

As far as I had come in beginning to understand lean, it was at this point in my journey that I received another valuable lesson from a colleague who taught through use of questions and by referring to an old TV show.

Chapter 2

Putting Strategy
back in Strategy
Deployment

*Starbucks has taken the ultimate commodity,
the coffee bean, and turned it into an
experience. We have taken the most personal
of experiences, healthcare, and turned it into a
commodity.*

—Brian Wong, MD
CEO, The Bedside Trust

A few years ago, I was sitting in the office of John Poole, senior vice president of the ThedaCare Improvement System, who was asking me a series of questions, each one designed to stimulate my thinking about lean without John ever making a didactic statement.

It might seem an odd approach from a burly ex-Navy pilot steeped in the traditions of the military, but it was totally consistent with John's challenging and inquiring mind. Unpretentious to a fault—his office walls and desk were bare, he never wore a tie, and his sport coat, which was used only for board meetings, hung from a hook—he spent most of his time at ThedaCare observing operations, asking discerning questions, and providing insightful comments that helped improve the daily implementation of lean. John told me he had to immerse himself in the operations because he was learning healthcare on the fly. His previous work experiences, besides the U.S. Navy, were at Goodwill Industries and in lean consulting.

When suddenly a connection occurred to me under John's gentle prodding, he would always smile slightly and say, "Ah, grasshopper, so you have learned something."

At first when John made this comment, I had to admit to some confusion. It wasn't until I remembered the old TV show called *Kung Fu* that I caught his meaning. *Kung Fu* was a 1970s series that followed the exploits of Kwai Chang Caine, a Shaolin monk who traveled through the Old West armed only with his spiritual training and his skill in the martial arts. In flashbacks we would see Caine as a small child absorbing lessons about life from Master Po, who would speak in aphorisms derived from Taoist philosophy. When Caine finally would understand one of Master Po's points, he would refer to the boy as "grasshopper" and praise his newfound learning.

At this particular session, Master Po, err John, had just asked me: When did you first understand that creating meaningful differentiation for patients was a result of redesigning processes rather than buying more assets? Under his gentle inquiry, I went back more than a decade— long before any knowledge about lean—to a bit of wisdom gleaned from a group of doctors in Appleton, Wisconsin.

In the mid-1990s, ThedaCare had successfully taken significant market share from our rival, Affinity Health System, by selling our health insurance plan to major local employers. Almost overnight, thousands of new patients joined our system. Affinity had relied heavily on urgent care centers to meet their patients' immediate medical concerns. When those patients switched to us, they wanted to know the locations of *our* urgent care centers. Unfortunately, we didn't have any.

As ThedaCare's senior vice president for strategy and marketing, my job was to help us figure out how to meet that need. We debated with senior leadership whether we should set up our own urgent care centers or ask one of our affiliated primary care practices to do that. I was convinced that we should have a medical practice affiliated with us, called Family Doctors, establish an urgent care clinic in the north Appleton area. In my mental model at the time, I thought that copying Affinity by building the same asset would meet our new patients' needs and allow us to focus on sustaining our competitive advantage of providing a better health insurance plan.

Family Doctors included about 25 physicians who had family practices in multiple locations in the Appleton area. They shared a billing service and waiting rooms, but they had their own offices, nurses, and schedulers. They wanted economies of scale while maintaining their autonomy as physicians.

Family Doctors had been instrumental in establishing the health insurance plan owned by many local physicians as well as ThedaCare. They provided a great deal of leadership in the governance and management of the health plan. From our point of view, we wanted them to become a more integrated part of our system because we were facing pressure from multiple sources for more accountability. At this time, President Bill Clinton and First Lady Hillary Clinton had launched their reform efforts at the federal level, Wisconsin

Governor Tommy Thompson had initiated his reform efforts at the state level, and local employers and insurers were demanding new exclusive contracts with guaranteed rate increases over three years.

With this in mind, I drove to the Family Doctors main office to press my case for urgent care during lunch with a number of the doctors. I had about 45 minutes to close the deal while the busy docs ate sandwiches and sipped sodas. Dr. Chuck McKee, then in his early 50s, listened intensely to what I was proposing. Chuck was a former Division III All-American quarterback at Lawrence University who was still in playing shape. You could easily imagine him barking out a play hunched over a center. When I finished, Chuck said, "Sounds like a marketing problem." What he meant was it was my problem, not theirs.

He and the other doctors at the table contended that urgent care did not fit in their business model. They treated the whole family and wanted a deep relationship with their patients. They believed strongly that their patients wanted the same relationship.

They felt the system they had established for patient care was superior to the urgent care model. They prided themselves on the long-term trusting relationships they had built with the families, often serving multiple generations of the same family. At Family Doctors, if a patient could not see his or her physician immediately, another physician or "teammate" from the same practice would examine the patient. This doctor would have in front of him or her the patient's medical records along with a familiarity with the patient's regular doctor's thinking and methods.

My mental model steered me to want to create a solution similar to our competitors', while our customer insights from market research supported the Family Doctors approach. Our research indicated that patients' number one concern was access to a doctor under urgent circumstances. They did not expect their doctor to be available 24 hours a day, 365 days a year. If they could not be examined by their doctor, they preferred to see a "teammate" rather than a "stranger" at an urgent care facility. In addition, our research showed that patients resented the long wait times that occurred at such facilities and disliked having to repeat information about their health background that was familiar to their regular doctor.

The Family Doctors business model had two problems, however. First, the group did not have a system where it could quickly enroll new patients. Second, there were not sufficient numbers of physicians to be teammates under urgent circumstances.

When Family Doctors confronted these issues, it decided to redesign its processes so that it could enroll new patients immediately. Patients in urgent circumstances then could gain access to a teammate physician the same day if their regular doctor was unavailable. Rather than build the same capacity as Affinity, these physicians had constructed a major competitive advantage by creating significantly greater value for their patients.

On reflection, I realized Dr. McKee was right. Family Doctors was focused on patients' needs and the operational process that would meet those needs. Without being formulated as such, it was a patient-centered strategic approach. This was another crack in my mental model.

Family Doctors was a real-world example of what I was learning about strategy in the mid-1990s from expert authors and practitioners: the importance of meaningful, sustainable differentiation. If you are not unique in a way that is relevant to customers, you become just another commodity, judged on price. I was also heavily influenced at the time by Michael Porter's 1996 article in *Harvard Business Review* where he said, "Competitive strategy is about being different. It means deliberately choosing a different set of activities to deliver a unique mix of value." The implication is that uniqueness is achieved by process innovation, not asset acquisition.

Family Doctors reinforced this learning from my exploration into cutting-edge strategic planning: understanding what patients as customers value and where they have unmet wants and needs. Competitive advantage is achieved through action, not words— process, not promises.

This view of strategy requires thinking of process as the basis for differentiation in the healthcare industry, which has traditionally seen asset acquisition as the strategic advantage. In my old way of thinking, that meant more urgent care clinics.

The healthcare industry during these years believed that competitive advantage was established by the number of buildings built, the amount of technology purchased, and the pool of talent recruited. The bill for all this spending was sent to insurance companies. Being familiar with creating competitive advantage in business, healthcare board members from the for-profit world often questioned this logic. They warned hospital managers of the risk of overinvesting in capital structure in an industry where volume and price were flattening. Such warnings often went unheeded.

Unfortunately, new warnings also go unheeded today. For example, Michael Sachs, chairman of TLSG, an early-stage venture firm focused on technology-enabled healthcare services, has argued that the healthcare industry is overly focused on 5% of the patient population, the heavy users, while ignoring the other 95%. These patients are an opportunity, he says, to create new delivery approaches since they are expressing the need for direct and simplified payment options, hours that matter to them when they need care, and more virtual care. This opportunity is particularly true for millennials, who will soon be the dominant market force in society. They have expressed striking new needs: 74% factor in online scheduling when choosing a provider, 76% look at online reviews when choosing a provider, and 60% prefer a virtual health option over a visit to a clinic.

I also want to clarify that differentiation is about what makes you unique. The need to be unique is universal, whether you are a healthcare organization in America, Canada, Great Britain, or South Africa. Any human service agency needs to be unique. The question every organization needs to ask is "What do I do for my customers that provides a unique value that they cannot get anywhere else?" If I can design a process that delivers that unique, relevant value, then customers will seek it out, and payers will be willing to pay for their customers to access it.

Any organization can make many potential process changes to create unique value, but it can apply only so many resources at any given time. Any organization must make strategic choices between all the possible improvements that it thinks could bring the most value to customers, to get us closer to what, in lean thinking, is called True North.

True North is the measure of a successful ideal state—a healthy organization that creates value for customers and society. True North is the handful of metrics that tell you whether the organization is winning or losing. Together, True North and organizational vision provide a guiding star for everyone to connect his or her work to what the leaders believe is important.

When we first began our lean journey at ThedaCare, we believed that lean thinking would be our source of differentiation and would create our ability to win because it enabled us to rethink our processes from the customer's point of view to produce greater value that is meaningful, relevant, and sustainable to him or her.

For a few years, this worked because other healthcare organizations were not adopting lean. Employers responded well to our pitch, and our market share increased. But then our competitors began catching up by significantly improving processes; they greatly eroded our competitive advantage.

So we now looked for our customers' biggest pain points, which led us to the concept of horizontal value creation for a prototypical patient we called Lori. This hypothetical patient and the scenarios that involved her would help the segment of patients with the most serious medical conditions navigate a complex system of care. We used segmentation and targeting customer research to identify Lori, then looked at the care delivery process from her point of view. At first we went too big and tried to make changes in too many specialty and primary care service lines; then we scaled it down and made choices. I will talk more about Lori later in the book.

This process of thinking enabled us to achieve a breakthrough—it is the combination of strategy deployment, operational effectiveness, and big rocks that gets an organization closer to its vision of True North. That combination of work had to be managed, and choices had to be made so we could maintain our focus. This improved our passion for change despite continued efforts by individuals within the organization who continued to advocate for their individual priorities.

As senior leaders at ThedaCare, we had to *choose and manage* work in order to achieve True North. I and the other senior leaders at ThedaCare had to pick the right balance of improving the current care models (operational effectiveness), of developing new care models intended to create unique customer value (strategy deployment), and of implementing big-rocks projects that must be done just to stay in business.

Figure 2.1. True North Equation

Leading an organization toward True North requires an executive team that picks the right things to work on, that aligns the organization's resources to get them done, and that manages the learning process in a positive, reinforcing loop that propels them closer and closer to the chosen ideal state.

We've already discussed that True North is the handful of metrics that tell everyone whether we are winning or losing. Examples of these metrics at ThedaCare included the number of patient safety incidents, employee turnover, and revenue per full-time equivalent (a measure of productivity). Executive teams must establish these metrics; in an environment where there are typically hundreds of measures, it's hard to choose. But it is critical to do it; otherwise, there is no direction for anyone.

Operational effectiveness is the outcome of a management system (see chapter 9) that is focused on developing problem solvers at the front line. Frontline workers can create more customer value by improving care model processes every day. This system does not wait until the manager weighs in. Problems are addressed immediately by the workers who know the work the best. It requires managers to teach and coach problem solving rather than do the problem solving themselves.

Big rocks can get in the way of differentiation. For example, just converting to an electronic health record system—a big rock—will not create differentiation. All health systems are buying and installing such systems. How an organization *uses* its electronic health record in its process might produce differentiation, however. Another example of a big rock is ICD-10 (the tenth revision of the International Statistical Classification of Disease and Related Health Problems from the World Health Organization). This update had to be done; it was a requirement of doing business. It sure didn't feel like continuous daily improvement associated with operational effectiveness, however, and it was not going to create differentiation because everyone had to do it—so it was a big rock.

Strategy deployment is the process by which top-level executives create and appraise the rest of the organization of a breakthrough strategy for success. But to work, it must be rigorously informed by what is occurring at the work level. So there is a component of bottom up to strategy deployment as well. Executives must go to the place of work and observe the work processes. They must interview customers, and they must discuss with frontline teams the barriers to delivering great care. It is very difficult to create the capacity for strategy deployment in healthcare because there are so many operational improvement priorities and big rocks being handed to leaders and to frontline teams. These projects can consume tremendous amounts of energy if choices are not made and managed.

How does a healthcare organization balance strategy deployment with operational effectiveness and big rocks?

One of the best examples I know of creating this balance is North Memorial Health Care, located in Robbinsdale, Minnesota, about 20 miles from Minneapolis.

Established in 1939 as Victory Hospital, it was a pioneer in health services—the first medical center outside of the Twin Cities—and it developed the first hospital-based medical transportation system involving helicopters, ambulances, and support staff.

Today, North Memorial Health at Robbinsdale (and a second hospital at Maple Grove, MN) is a level 1 trauma center and has received numerous awards for its high-quality patient care and for outstanding performance in areas such as hip and knee replacements, strokes, and heart attacks. Healthgrades has named it one of the top 50 hospitals in America for two years in a row. The hospital has advanced specialty centers, ranging from heart attacks to cancer, in a variety of locations from Twin City suburbs to western Wisconsin. It has plans to add a transitional care program, staffed with more than 30 nurses, to assist with those who are transitioning from the hospital to the home.

In addition to these accomplishments, North Memorial has been involved in an extensive strategic effort during the past few years under the leadership of CEO J. Kevin Croston, MD. Nearing 60, Kevin was a surgeon for nearly 30 years, of which 20 were at North Memorial. Kevin is a very good listener—he truly focuses on what his teams are saying.

In the six months prior to Kevin's taking over as CEO, Tiffany Zitzewitz, North Memorial's vice president for marketing, tried to design a growth strategy for North Memorial to differentiate the system from others in the area. At that time, North Memorial was constructing a new hospital building, and it had acquired several failing primary care clinics. Its focus was on being a trauma and emergency care hospital. A conflict developed over future direction: some senior leaders wanted to build the capabilities for population health management, others argued for an increase in hospital volume, and still others fought to redistribute services between the two hospitals. This is typical: different members of a senior leadership team have multiple, conflicting goals. And in the middle of this was Tiffany. She was trying to get them to segment and target patients and design a unique value proposition that would solve an unmet need of patients they were intending to serve.

Given all of this, Tiffany wanted to create a new brand, a new mission statement, and a new set of values. Tiffany is very energetic, outgoing, and highly committed to making change happen. The market research she conducted indicated that a distinct segment of patients—across all age and demographic groups—wanted to be more in charge of their medical experience in a variety of ways. Based on this information, Tiffany reconceptualized them from patients to customers and imagined an experience where the organization created what she called health pilots. Like the business model of Family Doctors, in her new model Tiffany wanted to establish a deep relationship with health pilots and patients to truly understand what patients desired out of their medical experience.

To achieve her goal, she believed a significant shift in the thinking and the behavior of the staff was required. When Kevin became CEO, he fully supported Tiffany's transformational efforts.

In 2015 Tiffany found an ally in Kelly Macken-Marble, vice president of outpatient operations. Together they wanted to create a unique value for Kelly's patients, and they both recognized the need to choose among competing priorities. Based on Tiffany's marketing research, she and Kelly were convinced that North Memorial could fill an open space in the market. But Kelly, who had experience with lean thinking from another organization, commented, "We say we are doing strategy deployment, but I don't see us deploying strategy." What she meant was that they were deploying broad categories of operational effectiveness initiatives, but they were not deploying anything different from their competitors that would be a unique value proposition for their customers. The lesson from Family Doctors again.

Kevin agreed with Tiffany's and Kelly's perceptions about strategy. He said he was frustrated that his organization had so many competing priorities. He believed this lack of focus was overburdening North Memorial. A recent downsizing had deprived the hospital of some highly qualified individuals, which had also increased the stress on the staff. Further, he thought North Memorial was not improving its operating performance and its margins were shrinking dramatically.

Over two years, Tiffany and Kelly, working with other senior leaders, began to change North Memorial's strategy. First, they framed North Memorial's business model and market position, which together comprised its current state. Then they outlined other potential business models: focusing on population health management, growing hospital volumes, or establishing a unique relationship with customers. These were the alternative future states. The problem to solve became choosing a preferred target state and developing a strategy to achieve it.

Next, they determined North Memorial's True North. They had to think about some important questions: What would winning look like? Where should North Memorial play? What is North Memorial's competitive advantage? What are its management capabilities? Senior leaders had to develop a hypothesis and a plan for how they would put it into action.

The senior leaders then selected what they were going to propose for strategic breakthrough experiments (and what they would set aside for now), and they picked what big rocks they wanted to accomplish in the next year—and, more importantly, those they could defer.

Ultimately, three experiments emerged. One experiment was to build on Tiffany's work and create health pilots at one site. Another experiment was to design easier transitions of care for very sick patients who required the involvement of many healthcare professionals before, during, and after hospitalization. Finally, one experiment was to create points of access to North Memorial through Hy-Vee grocery stores where a nurse practitioner would handle routine and limited heath concerns.

To clarify, an experiment differs from an initiative. For example, Tiffany's original hypothesis for serving the needs of health pilots would have required hiring scores of individuals to provide this intimate service to patients. In my old strategic thinking world, that's what would have happened. But by converting this hypothesis to an experiment, they built out this solution, starting with a minimum viable product in one location.

In the fall of 2016, senior leaders further developed their earlier work. They developed the next set of strategic initiatives and big rocks and decided what they could defer. In particular, this meant fitting in the big rocks of revenue cycle management and the distribution of clinical services at their two hospitals.

A recent conversation with Kevin revealed that he felt North Memorial had made substantial progress, and he termed his experience using the strategic management system as "Fabulous!" Before the planning process, he thought that North Memorial was trying to do too many things at the same time. The lean way of thinking changed this. He said, "The process requires the entire team to act in a focused way and the discipline to stay on it until better outcomes are achieved for both staff and customers. It helps staff find their roles and what they have to do. And it forces decisions to be made that reduce variation."

He believes that healthcare as an industry doesn't like to change, particularly in regard to new processes. But North Memorial's experience with this strategic management system is that it empowers and trains staff to do what they have to do to satisfy customers.

For him, lean thinking and methods made a big difference in customers' lives, which to him "is why we all got into healthcare in the first place. When healthcare is done correctly, it is a pathway to something joyful."

The strategic management system that the leaders at North Memorial experienced is based on PDSA thinking, and it addresses problems at every level of a healthcare organization, from caring for the unique needs of individual patients to handling the unique needs of the organization.

In the next part of this book, I explain in depth *how* this system, illustrated in Figure 2.2, works. Chapter 3 describes the process for understanding your current organizational reality. Chapter 4 is about identifying the problem or opportunity to be solved. Chapter 5 looks at methods for making strategic choices. Chapter 6 outlines how to deploy these hypothetical solutions using lean learning loops, and chapter 7 explains the process known as "catch–ball" for aligning strategic intent throughout the organization. Chapter 8 details a process for managing this work to avoid "scope creep" and new initiatives dropping from the sky.

Learning this system will take time and practice, but with effort, it will open up a new approach to strategic thinking. By the end of this section, hopefully, both John Poole and Master Po would be able to say, "Ah, grasshopper, you have learned something."

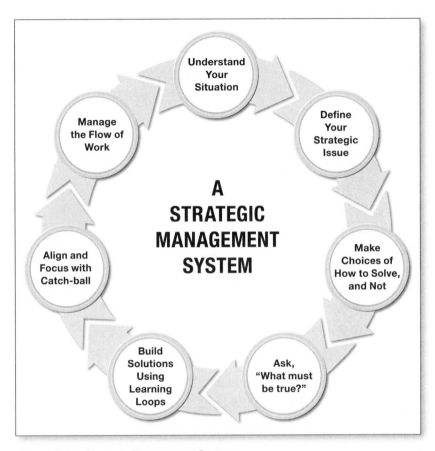

Figure 2.2. A Strategic Management System

Chapter **3**

Understanding
the Mess

Start from need.
—Taiichi Ohno

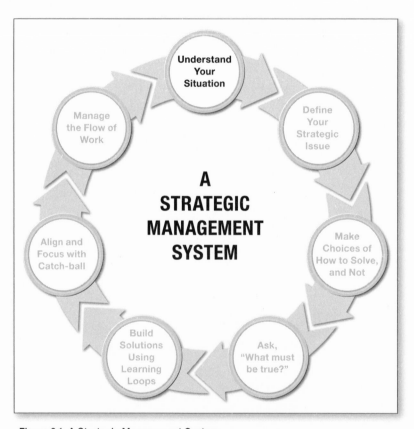

Figure 3.1. A Strategic Management System

For those of us who work in healthcare, there are many days that we feel that we are in a mess and we want someone, anyone, to save us from situations that seem forced on us. We yearn for an expert to hand us a model that will explain what famed psychologist William James called the "blooming, buzzing confusion."

I know that feeling, and I spent years learning the latest thinking about strategy and boldly proclaiming to senior leadership that I had the ideas and models that would cure the problems we confronted.

As my mental model began to crack more and more, I finally saw that whatever paradigm I learned and sought to present would be largely useless unless I could engage everyone from the front line to the CEO in a thorough discussion of these concepts and then get their whole-hearted participation using the strategic management system. In short, I had to help them crack their mental models and stop them from looking at me to be a strategic planning hero.

I also learned that when people felt they were in a mess, it was more than an emotional expression of being trapped in a dilemma. It is a term with a precise meaning used in systems thinking. Systems thinking is a management discipline that concerns an understanding of a system by examining the linkages and interactions between the components that comprise the entirety of that defined system. "The mess" is the word used to describe a chaotic, complex environment that involves interdependent variables; when you change one element, many other elements are impacted, and the nature of reality changes. Healthcare CEOs and senior leaders face this reality every day— every action starts a chain of reactions with consequences, many of which were unanticipated.

The healthcare industry is extremely complex, in part because it is subjected to major macro-changes such as the Clintons' reform efforts in the 1990s, Obamacare in 2009, and efforts to repeal and replace the Affordable Health Care Act in 2017. This last situation, which still has not been resolved as of this writing, has caused many healthcare organizations to freeze, unsure of what to do; other organizations are consolidating into larger systems, seeking protection from the uncertainty generated in Washington, D.C. Both responses most likely will be ineffective. When such conditions prevail in other industries, leaders focus on fostering better understanding of the customer and creating better products; they don't put decision making on hold or mindlessly consolidate.

Because such turbulence is beyond the control of any particular healthcare system, it is vitally important not to try to be a hero in this industry. Rather, you need to understand the mess through what Peter Senge calls "team learning, where the skills of groups of people look for the larger picture beyond individual perspectives."

That is why when I explain the plan portion of the PDSA cycle, I always start with background and current condition, trying to help others understand where they are today and how they got there. This awareness always involves breaking down old mental models often based on some notion of stability. Instead, they need a new mental model that involves a current, comprehensive, shared framing and understanding of reality, called a situation analysis or market position assessment.

In our old mental model prior to systems thinking, strategic planners like myself saw each market factor or force as an independent, static, predictable, and controllable variable. We would collect information and insights from internal sources and outside experts on each of these variables and synthesize them using a strengths, weaknesses, opportunities, and threats analysis. This would generate a list of key strategic issues, and we would develop prescriptive long-term plans to solve these issues based on our predictions of how well we would execute, how customers would respond, and how competitors would react.

In our new mental model, there is no such thing as perfect information. The market variables are interdependent, dynamic, and only somewhat predictable and controllable. This is true for clinicians in care delivery. When they perform a current state assessment of a patient and prescribe a plan, they cannot control every outcome, such as patient and family compliance. While strategic planners must strive to gain the most comprehensive and accurate insights we can gather, we must recognize they are informing our guess, not our ability to predetermine the future.

A market position assessment under these conditions requires as many people in the organization as possible to generate insights—bottom up and top down—about how to create unique value with patient segments and about the context in which the organization is trying to do it. The objective is comprehensive, current, shared understanding.

According to www.smartling.com, a market position assessment includes a deliberate branding process that is focused on consumer consciousness of the meanings and associations of a company's products. It is built on business data and is the statement that incorporates differentiation, distinction, and similarity in a brand narrative. It is a long-term effort to solidify a company's identity and its products or services in a unique space within the minds of a target audience.

At ThedaCare, senior leadership learned the techniques described in this chapter together at shared education sessions. We then practiced them together. It was critical to our ability to navigate through a very turbulent time between 2000 and 2003. Our shared understanding helped us immeasurably when we changed business models, sold our health plan, and focused on care delivery.

Moving from individual perceptions of reality to a shared one takes time, effort, patience, and respect for the opinions of others. I remember when Jim Matheson, ThedaCare's vice president of marketing, and I reported at a meeting on our new understandings about how to gain deep insights into the customer experience. We then proposed using this information to describe new customer segments, create new forms of customer delivery, and formulate new ways to communicate with our customers.

The resistance to our message was instant and formidable. The mental models in that room hinged on a concept of a healthcare system being all things to all people within a 45-mile radius. The senior leaders thought my job and Jim's were to package what the organization produced and then communicate it effectively to bring in more customers. Case closed. Jim and I suggested that we had to start from our customers' needs and be aware that there were many customer segments. We proposed to target a subset of customers with different value propositions. This was anathema to many. It took a number of sessions for their mental models to begin to crack. And it happened only through long discussions about the reality that ThedaCare faced and what would work best in this continually changing environment.

As I introduce a number of concepts, models, and strategic tools in this chapter, remember that the key point is that they *must* be discussed with others and thoroughly thought through as to how they apply to your healthcare situation.

The leadership team needs to share a current, comprehensive understanding of the organization's present state that includes:

- Your transactional environment—the dynamic relationship between:

    o You and your customers, where you are trying to find and fill a need

    o You and your competitors, where you are trying to create a sustainable competitive advantage

    o Your competitors and your current and potential customers, where you are trying to anticipate and become a first-mover

- The industry in which this transactional environment resides

- The macro-environmental factors and forces that shape the structure of your industry.

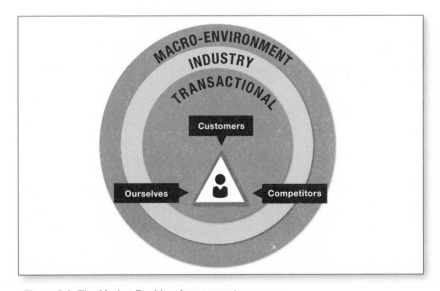

Figure 3.2. The Market Position Assessment

All of these relationships are changing second by second. At ThedaCare, my job was to think strategy every day. The system leadership team talked strategy every week. We engaged the board of trustees in a discussion of critical strategic uncertainties at every board meeting. In addition, once a year we would put together a written market position assessment and discuss it with major stakeholder groups and then with the board. After receiving the board's advice, we would adjust our deployment of that strategy and write it into a strategic plan. Knowing that the written plan was outdated instantly, we continued to find new ways to refresh our shared understanding of our current state.

I found a number of strategic management tools that really helped me understand the three dimensions of the market position.

To Understand the Transactional Environment: Start from Need

As implied in the quote above by Taiichi Ohno—considered the father of the Toyota Production System, known as lean—senior leaders need to have deep understanding of what customers value and the pain points that are keeping them from realizing that value.

To begin to understand your business model, you need to understand your customer. Until recently, the healthcare industry has relied on traditional customer research methods such as telephone, written, and computer-assisted surveys; focus groups; and patient panels in person or online. All ask questions about what a consumer *might* do in a particular situation. The mental models adhered to by senior leaders at ThedaCare had long believed in the efficacy of these approaches. And I did too for a long time.

But as I continued my journey of learning, I became a proponent of the ethnographic research approach used in design thinking. This is what Jim Matheson and I were discussing with the ThedaCare senior leadership. With this approach, you try to understand how customers think and what they say and do as you observe them in real situations. This is how innovators discover latent and emergent needs. The Disney Company is heavily influenced by this source of information about customers. Their employees are called on to feed back to senior leaders their observations about customers and their concerns.

I was first introduced to this way of thinking in the late 1990s. Our senior leadership team participated in Disney's customer experience training in Orlando, Florida. During one of our learning sessions, a frontline employee described how she innovated new ways to create customer value. While doing her job, she would observe customer pain points and try something small (minimum viable product) to see whether it alleviated them. If not, she would pivot and try something else. If it helped, she would persevere with her idea, working with other team members to build it out with successive additional features until positive change was adopted and spread throughout the work team. This approach is how Disney discovered that putting up signs telling patrons how long it takes to get to the front of a line helped reduce customer anxiety. This idea did not come from a C-suite executive armed with sophisticated market research.

You will see most experiments in healthcare organizations using design thinking applied to outpatient care delivery. My first experience with design thinking was at ThedaCare, with our breakthrough initiative called Care Team Redesign. We tried to figure out whether we could help the chronically sickest patients in our ThedaCare Physicians practices with an entirely new model of care delivery involving team members in completely different ways. We would go into a patient's home and understand life from the patient's perspective, and we would try new experiments that would enable the patient to manage his or her disease and live a healthier life. Some of these experiments involved using new home technology; we had to learn what it would take for patients to adopt the use of the technology. We would make small changes with which members of the care team would interact with patients and how they would interact with them in the office. Each of these was a rigorous experiment so we could measure what created value and what did not.

This continuous process of deeply understanding patients' expressed and latent needs, trying interventional experiments in process redesign, and observing customers' reactions so we could pivot or persevere led to new insights that were fed back into the strategic planning process. These insights could then be shared with customers of other service lines, such as cardiology, where there were a significant number of chronically ill patients. This is the critical step—to gather and share the insights so that the organization's understanding of the overall market situation could be improved.

The Business Model Canvas, developed by Alex Osterwalder and available at Strategyzer.com, is a tool for understanding what makes your organization unique and how you can translate that knowledge into a financially stable enterprise. This is especially important when making fundamental changes to your business model. When I have used this tool in industries other than healthcare, the leadership teams seem to have a much deeper shared knowledge of their own business model and that of their competitors. When considering changes to your business model, learn what it is you do that creates unique relationships with customers in a financially sustainable way.

Organizations that now are converting "from volume to value" by taking risk for the health of whole populations tend to add costly new activities and resources to their cost structure yet drive down their revenue. Unless you are a prepaid health plan business model such as Kaiser, this can present significant problems. Marshfield Clinic, a health system in Wisconsin that I have great admiration for, did precisely that. Although the company owned a health insurance plan, the majority of its revenue came from fees for services from patients outside the health plan. Marshfield Clinic became a participant in the Physician Group Practice Demonstration Project under Medicare, a shared savings–type structure, and was consistently among the top performers in the country in that project. It saved Medicare millions of dollars, and Marshfield was rewarded by being able to keep a portion of those savings.

Unfortunately, the shared savings it received were substantially less than the lost fee-for-service revenue from patients who avoided procedures. The reward for doing the right thing for all the right reasons resulted in Marshfield laying off about 200 employees and in other staff members taking a 15% pay cut. I'm not saying "Don't change your business model." I'm suggesting that as healthcare organizations develop new value propositions, they must have a thorough understanding of what they are changing.

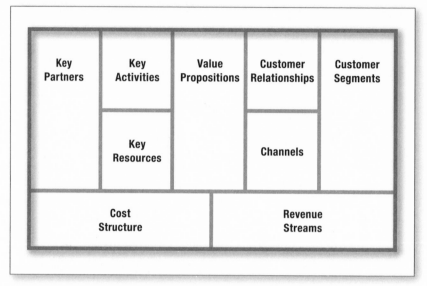

Figure 3.3. Business Model Canvas
Source: Strategyzer.com

Once you understand your business model, apply the same tool to understanding your competitors' business models. You will then be able to gauge your sources of competitive advantage and not to underestimate their competitive advantages. If you don't do this exercise, you may make false assumptions about your strengths and their weaknesses, which may ultimately lead to failed initiatives.

Understand the Context of Your Industry

Harvard Business School Professor Michael Porter's Five Forces model has long been used to understand industry structure and the potential for disruptive new business models entering a competitor's arena. Porter's five forces include the traditional rivalry between existing industry competitors; two forces from "vertical" competition: the threat of new entrants and the threat of new products or services;

and two forces from "horizontal" competition: the bargaining power of suppliers and the bargaining power of customers.

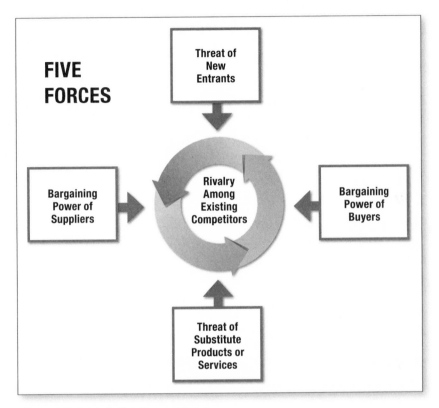

Figure 3.4. Porter's Five Forces Model

A change in any of the forces normally requires a business unit to reassess the marketplace given the overall change in industry structure. This tool's original purpose was to help analyze the attractiveness of an industry from the perspective of an investment opportunity by replying to this question: What are the potential financial returns if one is to enter, or stay in, a chosen industry?

When healthcare leadership teams use this tool, it helps them to step outside of the transactional arena that they know and to identify potential competitive forces that they may not know of *yet*. From my experience, it brings a certain humility to leadership teams: when teams are honest with each other, it keeps them from overestimating their current competitive position.

For example, it helped us at ThedaCare to understand the potential impact of a freestanding imaging service that was going to enter our market. While most other healthcare systems chose to compete with that new entrant, we chose to partner with them so that we could learn from their business model.

Understand the Macro-Environmental Factors and Forces Impacting Your Industry

PESTLE analysis is a great interactive tool for teams to identify the political, economic, social, technological, legal, and environmental forces that impact an organization and industry. The exercise involves acquiring the perspectives from many people in many industries and then generating a wide variety of forces that interdependently impact the demand and supply conditions within your industry. This is a great input into scenario planning, an exercise in which a team of internal and external stakeholders tries to create different potential futures by understanding the above factors and forces. Since no one can predict the future, building fictional futures may be helpful in testing organizational strategic ideas.

At the time John and I were first studying scenario planning, some of the largest corporations in the world were using it, including Disney,

Accenture, Motorola, and Royal Dutch Shell. These companies and others were increasingly dissatisfied with the existing ways of planning. Many realized how misleading predictions could be when based on straight-line extrapolations from the past.

We enacted scenario planning at ThedaCare by putting together a team of individuals from our organization and thought leaders from other organizations. The process of scenario planning begins with a long discussion about how the participants think big shifts in society, economics, politics, and technology might affect a particular issue. From this, the group identifies critical uncertainties, including things that will have the most impact on the issue under discussion and those whose outcome is the most uncertain. These critical uncertainties are used to create alternative scenarios. Then the team tests different hypothetical strategies in the context of the scenarios. The hypothesis that seems to work in all the generated future uncertain worlds is considered the most robust strategy.

The trick is not the development of the scenarios but how you use them to engage stakeholders in the organization in strategic discussions. Don't argue over who has the best scenario or which scenario people like the best. Foster discussions about the meaning of world events and how they can impact the industry and the organization. Since no one can predict the future or predetermine every outcome, it encourages teams to respectfully talk about what could happen and what we could do under those circumstances. This is an exercise in which people enjoy the interactive dialogue. It builds flexibility in thinking among teammates and encourages them to problem solve together.

Beware of the Limitations of the SWOT Analysis

As described before, when teams have assembled all the points of information from the transactional environment, as well as industry-level and macro-environmental perspectives, the next step has traditionally been a strengths, weaknesses, opportunities, and threats (SWOT) analysis. I never particularly enjoyed them, because I personally found that they revealed only superficial information. If leaders were in the room, a strength was invariably, "We have a great leadership team." When I couldn't take any more of those types of exercises, I added the following four rules to try to make it more insightful:

- A strength is in the eyes of your customers compared to your competitors; show me the data.

- A weakness is in the eyes of your customers compared to your competitors; show me the data.

- An opportunity exists in the marketplace; it is available to your competitors as well as you.

- A threat exists in the marketplace; it impacts your competitors as well as you.

While it is a popular tool that can help synthesize a great deal of information and it can be a very interactive exercise that gets people to think together, SWOT's real problem is that it keeps your thinking inside the box you know rather than moving your thinking about latent and emerging customer needs and lurking competitive threats outside that box. It is more helpful in the context of specific situations where you are trying to understand the market position of a specific value proposition with a target population.

In this chapter I have laid out how to think about the current state of a business. I've introduced some of the tools in the strategic management tool box. But I believe that deeply understanding unmet customer needs is where you must start when trying to understand the current state. This is best discovered through ethnographic research in which you are engaging with customers directly through observation and individual interviews. You also must deeply understand the current state of the business. I believe the best way to do this is through the business model canvas, which forces you to ask critical questions about your industry and the environment you are in. These are the first steps in the strategic management system. Since that current state is inherently dynamic and ever-changing, you need to have a process to keep it fresh. Constantly engaging with customers and frontline staff and regularly revisiting the current state of business questions are the methods that we found worked for us at ThedaCare. Now let's explore the next step in the strategic management system: the process for envisioning the ideal state.

Chapter **4**

Framing
the Strategic Issue

The formulation of the problem is often more essential than its solution.

—Albert Einstein

Figure 4.1. A Strategic Management System

A strategic management system enables leadership teams to choose wisely and execute thoughtfully. It is built on the foundation of PDSA thinking. You activate it by framing the strategic issue facing your organization—which can be seen as either a compelling problem or an exciting opportunity. Framing is achieved by:

- Understanding your organization's *current situation* and how you got to this point.

- Fixing your eyes on *the ideal state*, i.e., the ultimate picture of a healthy, successful organization creating unique and relevant value for patients. The ideal state can be a combination of the organization's vision (what winning looks like) and True North metrics (how you know whether you're winning).

- Keeping that ideal state in mind and then asking: What is *the gap from the current state to the ideal state*? Given that gap, what is the problem, the opportunity, or the strategic issue you must handle first?

- Maintaining the ideal state and strategic issue in your mind and then asking: *What is the next achievable target state*? What is the next best step toward that ideal state where your strategic issue is resolved?

Traditionally, healthcare teams enjoy talking about the ideal state and are fairly good at describing what the ideal state could look like. They call it a vision statement. Most of the time this ideal state is guided only by intuition, without any deep knowledge of what the customer really needs. The description also tends to be very broad, all-inclusive, and not significantly different from those of other organizations. Because of this, teams can get bogged down when trying to figure out what to do next.

I had the same difficulty. Like most senior leaders, I wanted to stay at a high level, using my intuition to sense an opportunity and to think broadly about what would be required to get there, and then leave the details to others. My mental model made it difficult for my direct reports to accomplish objectives in a timely manner since I did not help them frame the strategic issue and then work with them to solve it.

Many years back, when we at ThedaCare were wrestling with the selection and prioritization of strategic issues, I stumbled across this parable while searching the Internet. Like all important parables, it told a universal truth.

"A professor stood before his philosophy class and had some items in front of him. When the class began, he wordlessly picked up a very large and empty mayonnaise jar and proceeded to fill it with golf balls. He then asked the students if the jar was full. They agreed that it was.

The professor then picked up a box of pebbles and poured them into the jar. He shook the jar lightly. The pebbles rolled into the open areas between the golf balls. He then asked the students again if the jar was full. They agreed it was.

The professor next picked up a box of sand and poured it into the jar. Of course, the sand filled up everything else. He asked once more if the jar was full. The students responded with a unanimous 'yes.'

The professor then produced two cups of coffee from under the table and poured the entire contents into the jar, effectively filling the empty space between the sand. The students laughed.

Now, said the professor as the laughter subsided, 'I want you to recognize that this jar represents your life. The golf balls are the important things—God, your family, your children, your health, your friends, and your favorite passions—and if everything else was lost and only they remained, your life would still be full. The pebbles are the other things that matter, like your job, your house, and your car. The sand is everything else—the small stuff.

'If you put the sand into the jar first,' he continued, 'there is no room for the pebbles or the golf balls. The same goes for life. If you spend all your time and energy on the small stuff, you will never have room for the things that are important to you.

'Pay attention to the things that are critical to your happiness. Play with your children. Take time to get medical checkups. Take your spouse out to dinner. Play another 18. There will always be time to clean the house and fix the disposal. Take care of the golf balls first—the things that really matter. Set your priorities. The rest is just sand.'

One of the students raised her hand and inquired what the coffee represented. The professor smiled. 'I'm glad you asked. It just goes to show you that no matter how full your life may seem, there's always room for a couple of cups of coffee with a friend.'"

CEOs and senior leaders of healthcare systems have the daunting task of helping others in the organization decide what are golf balls, what are pebbles, and what is sand. This is where the lack of choice making starts and overburden begins. These senior executives often assign their staffs too many priorities because they describe all the things needed to close the gap between their current state and the ideal state. Like me, they learned this old mental model at long-range strategic planning events where we would list all the things we might have to do in the next three to five years to achieve an ideal state. Every professional in care delivery—doctor, nurse, therapist, and technologist—is already fully engaged in how to support a patient's achieving a better state of health. The more initiatives that are forced on them from the top, the less well they can perform their value-creating work.

In any healthcare organization, there is no shortage of potential problems to solve or opportunities to capitalize on. The strategic question is: What are the most important initiatives to work on now, and which can be deferred?

The strategic issue is the compelling problem or opportunity that you are solving for. The process of framing the strategic issue starts with a shared understanding of your current state (the subject of chapter 3), defining a shared vision and detail of your ideal state, seeing the gap between the two, and identifying the problem or opportunity.

I have encountered numerous strategic issues within healthcare systems and the for-profit and nonprofit companies that I work with, which include:

- A manufacturing company that needed to diversify its business-to-business customer base because 50% of its revenue came from a single customer and 65% of its revenue was derived from a very volatile industry. This led to wild swings in its year-to-year financial performance and employee turnover.

- An engineering consulting firm where, as a young engineer told me, "Eighty percent of what I do today that we charge for will get Googled for free within 10 years."

- An engineering services company that wanted to double its size but had 70% of its margin coming from a distribution business. It believed that the distribution business would be "Amazon.commed" and have all the margins driven out of it within five years.

- A human services organization at full capacity and with a perpetual waiting list that needed to serve more customers without adding physical capacity. It needed to radically redesign the process by which it served customers.

Picture the Ideal State

An effective strategic management system encourages a shared vision of an ideal state. In fact, employees' and senior leaders' personal missions must be aligned with the organization's vision. But while you share a vision, you cannot predetermine exactly the path to accomplishing this goal. Rather, you must learn together what it will take to get there.

Vision statements have been used by many for decades, often detailing a desired future. But vision statements are usually not very descriptive of the ideal state. Lean organizations put much more rigor into describing what the ideal state should look like. The ideal state is defined through not only words but also specific metrics. The ideal state is measured by True North metrics, which are the handful of measures that help to define winning and losing.

In this process of discovery, I have found Lafley and Martin's "winning aspiration" terminology helpful: "What does winning look like, with customers and against competitors; and how would you know if you are winning?" This helps healthcare organizations make choices about understanding customer segmentation and creating meaningful differentiation.

Two examples provide guidance.

For North Memorial, winning is defined through the customer's eyes in its mission statement:

By providing better experiences, where you are in control, you can live your most vibrant life. We know good health is at the root of our well-being, but can a healthcare system make healthcare … healthier? We say yes.

For ThedaCare, winning is very specifically focused on "delivering better patient value" and is measured by a balance of zero defects in safety and quality, 100% employee engagement, 100% customer loyalty, and financial performance that stays between the upper and lower limits assigned by the board.

Mission statements are often taken for granted because they seem so similar. They invariably describe why an organization exists and the role that its founders expected it to fulfill, which is usually "to improve the health of the communities we serve." Mission is not the basis for differentiation; differentiation is achieved by *how* each organization accomplishes its mission.

However, mission becomes important as a reminder of why healthcare professionals go to work. Each professional has a personal mission, the role in society he or she aspires to fill, and the reason why he or she does what he or she does. If the organization's mission conflicts with the professional's mission, or if it behaves in a way that conflicts with its mission, professionals often become disengaged. For example, disengagement can happen if a hospital aspires to benefit society yet its priorities reflect only a desire for financial growth and profitability; employees may question the motives of leaders if the hospital emphasizes improving community health yet all of its metrics and priorities indicate high volumes of sickness care.

We realized at ThedaCare that if we wanted the full participation of our employees in any new strategic initiatives and if we wanted to truly be listening to our customers' needs, we had to create an effective and authentic mission. We had to determine collectively what winning was and how we would achieve it.

ThedaCare addressed this issue in 2010 at a board of trustees meeting convened to discuss success metrics. I presented the annual strategic plan update and described our priorities but didn't set any five-year market share targets for services and service lines. Some board members who worked in private industry told me that they were accustomed to seeing sales and market share targets for products and services. At this point, our strategic plan called for reducing the incidence of cardiovascular disease in the local population. The private-sector board members then asked: What are the market share targets for open-heart surgery in five years? Other board members who were more interested in measuring our lean journey in process advances and community health improvement asked: Why would we aspire to increase the need for open-heart surgery?

Over the next four months, we as a group discussed, debated, challenged, and argued how best to answer these questions. As the conversations continued, board members asked deeper questions: Why did the organization exist? Were we delivering on the promise made to the community when the organization was formed?

Board Chair Walter Rugland, Vice Chair Jon Stellmacher, and I were tasked with leading the discussions. We initially researched how similar healthcare organizations with a similar mission of community health improvement delivered on their promises. We specifically researched the use of balanced scorecards in not-for-profit organizations. What we found was striking: balanced scorecards for not-for-profit organizations looked just like those of for-profit organizations. Financial metrics such as growth and profitability were the primary measures of success. What surfaced over and over was the old concept of the organization as biologic being: "If you're not growing, you're dying."

After these months of discussions, the ThedaCare board settled on four dimensions of success that were expressed in specific statements and metrics and were the foundation of the ideal state they envisioned. It was the core of how they would know whether management was delivering on the mission: to improve the health of our communities.

- *Evidence of continual improvement in community health.* ThedaCare was not the only organization responsible and accountable for this; many other community agencies needed to be involved. But the board expected us to be *leaders* in the effort. Our success could be measured using county health rankings, an annual assessment resulting from a partnership between the University of Wisconsin Population Health Institute and the Robert Wood Johnson Foundation.

- *Leadership in improving the overall value of healthcare locally and nationally.* The board founded a separate organization, the ThedaCare Center for Healthcare Value (now called Catalysis), to provide national leadership on three core issues of health reform needed to deliver better patient value. The board anointed John Toussaint as its inaugural CEO. This not-for-profit education institute focused on transparency of healthcare performance, payment systems that reward better value, and care delivery designed around the patient, not the provider.

Over the past decade, Catalysis has brought together a large community of leaders throughout the world and has impacted hundreds of health systems.

- *Access to coordinated care without regard to socioeconomic status.* In addition to serving patients regardless of ability to pay, the board expected us to create continuity of care by pioneering the use of electronic health records and processes that would keep patients from being dropped through the cracks. We initially measured this through the extent of our electronic health connectivity with a wide network of employed and affiliated providers so that our patients' experience would be seamless.

- *Prudence in financial oversight.* While the community expected us to generate margins that would keep us financially stable and self-sufficient, the board also set expectations for how much is too much. They established upper and lower limits for operating margin, cash on hand, and debt service coverage. The board created upper limits because open-ended financial growth and profit were *not* primary success measures.

Mission now took on a whole new meaning for ThedaCare. These dimensions and metrics of mission effectiveness became important criteria in major decisions from the board and with senior leaders. While we are in a competitive marketplace, we never lose sight of *why* we exist: to serve the community in important and measurable ways.

This exercise at ThedaCare, although long and extensive, resulted in a much more specific notion of what an ideal state would look like and an increased desire to achieve it. We could envision winning through a combination of mission and vision, and we would know whether we were winning through True North metrics.

Practice Idealized Design

The actual process of determining the gap between current state and ideal state is messy, but Jamshid Gharajedaghi, an organizational theorist and management consultant, created a step-by-step way of thinking that helped me break my old mental model about how to deal with the gap between the current state and the ideal state. This includes:

- Understanding your current situation

- Framing your ideal state, your vision of perfection

- Determining how to get closer to the ideal state through a series of what he calls "successive approximations." These approximations are influenced by frontline observations, patient feedback, environmental changes, and competitor behavior. With each one, you identify the next target state and experiment your way there. Once the new state is stabilized with standard work so the organization will not slip back, it becomes your new current state.

- After achieving a stable, new current state, look again at the ideal state to see whether it has shifted in the meantime. Since time has passed, customers and competitors have created a new reality. Once you refocus on where the ideal state is, set your sights on the next target state and the succeeding steps to get there.

Getting closer to the ideal state through successive approximations is what Gharajedaghi calls idealized design. Setting the next target state, the next major step toward the ideal state, allows you and your team to focus on an objective they can see and get their arms around. It is a practical stage for making the choices necessary for how to get there. In both idealized design and design thinking, you take a big, important step toward the future while knowing risk is involved, but you have a disciplined method of experimentation that helps you find the solution.

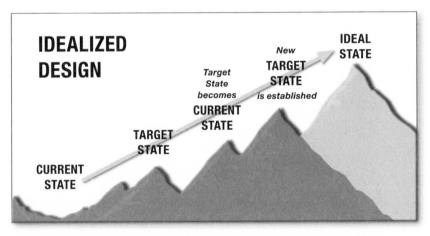

Figure 4.2. Idealized Design

This takes repetitive practice, but the concept of distinguishing target state from ideal state helped us see process redesign from a patient's perspective. With idealized design, we were asking potential patients or past patients how they wanted to experience their care. We became much more interested in what was being observed by frontline workers. From these observations and interviews came a target state that was patient centered. Now teams could get their arms around a more tangible objective and generate more definitive expectations of how to get there.

Since healthcare systems are complex organizations, it can be a challenge to get your arms around the myriad of strategic issues at any given time and make choices of which key strategic issues to address at any given time. With each chosen issue, you must define the gap between current state and target state to provide guidance to the team in your organization that is going to try to solve the problem or opportunity. At ThedaCare, we worked with Sg2, a leading healthcare analytics and consultancy firm, to develop a spreadsheet that helped us understand in financial terms the gap we needed to close between current and target states. This simple but elegant model uses the following formula:

population × use rate for a specific health service = market demand
× market share = our volume
× our price = our revenue
less: our cost = our margin

We would fill in actual performance from the previous year on all these dimensions. Then we would make assumptions for all these dimensions five years out. The difference would be the gap to close. Since in our market the population was not rapidly growing and use rates for hospital services were falling, demand was flat. Our "realized price" after discounts to payers was flat for three years in a row. Clearly, if we did not increase market share, our revenues would be flat.

Even though we had lowered our cost trend to 2.5% annually, the combination of flat revenues and rising costs would result in poor financial performance in a very short period of time. To compound the problem, we had a 60%–65% market share in most of our service areas. Some of our ThedaCare board business leaders told us that in their industries the cost of increasing market share from that level was often greater than the returns from the share we would gain. That gap in operating performance defined our strategic issue annually. In financial terms, it became our problem to solve in strategic planning.

I think the greatest benefit of this approach was the dialogue it created throughout the organization during the strategic planning process. Many people became involved in formulating each of the assumptions. This contributed to the concept I described in chapter 3 of a living, breathing market position assessment that tried to capture shared knowledge of a complex, dynamic, and unpredictable market.

Where Does Innovation Fit?

When helping organizations build their strategic management capability, I am frequently asked the following question by senior leaders: "How does innovation fit with strategic planning?" In the past few decades, innovation was not an important concern for strategic planners in traditional healthcare organizations. We focused on adding new capacity to meet increasing demand for services.

The pace of innovation from external disruptors has intensified greatly in recent years. Niche players and big-box retailers such as SmartChoice MRI and CVS pharmacies, as well as online and phone-based triage and treatment systems, have invaded the market. This pressure on traditional health systems has forced them to consider innovation more than ever. Disruption of an industry almost always comes from outside the industry. When Amazon, Berkshire Hathaway, and JPMorgan Chase announce that they are going to reinvent healthcare for their million-plus employees, healthcare CEOs and senior leaders may be prompted to innovate. Amazon knows how to use design thinking and other innovative approaches to disrupt industries. Prudence dictates their adoption by traditional healthcare providers.

I always had an interest in the topic of innovation, but only recently, after extensive new learnings, have I been able to answer this question with confidence. Matthew May was of immense help, particularly when he said innovative thinking and systems are required when "the solution to the strategic issue is a complete mystery." When you understand unmet customer needs and realize they are a key strategic issue but don't know yet how to find a solution, that's where you can use the principles, systems, and tools of innovation, such as design thinking. The strategic management system points the innovation process in the right direction of the strategic issue to be solved.

I also learned a great deal from Ted Toussaint and his experience at Atrius Health in Boston. Ted is John Toussaint's son, so he has been forced to listen to lean thinking talk most of his life. Ted is an innovation engineer and helped to set up the Innovation Office at Atrius. He provided me frameworks for understanding the nature of the problem or opportunity to be solved and what kind of problems required innovation thinking versus incremental improvement. In short, the more ambiguous or complex the problem is, the more it requires innovation. And innovation requires a defined process. It doesn't just happen.

Innovation has many definitions, but the one I like is "people using new knowledge and understanding to experiment with new possibilities in order to implement new concepts that create new value." Incumbent providers with long-standing business models often resist the introduction of innovation because it causes disruption of time-honored work flows. In the Innovation Office at

Atrius, the mantra was "Let's obsolete it." What the innovation team experienced was that existing structures and processes attempted to kill off internal change. This inertia is present in every organization. Change is difficult; radical change is even harder.

My experience was similar with ThedaCare Physicians. When Walgreens and Walmart introduced retail clinics in our market in 2000, ThedaCare Physicians' first reaction was to resist because this new business model could potentially cut the price of routine visits by 60%. Our physicians did not want to lose that revenue and see only very sick patients.

I remember being in a meeting of physicians where one doctor's response to this threat was to propose we run attack advertisements declaring these clinics were of low quality. He added that he thought ThedaCare should approach state regulators and have them legally restrict Walgreens' and Walmart's further entry into our market.

As we discussed these proposals, it was clear that substantial money would be wasted on advertising and in lobbying, with little positive effect on improving ThedaCare's position in the market. Instead, ThedaCare Physicians chose to innovate its business model by providing low-cost care in retail settings in a way that Walgreens and Walmart couldn't. As a franchisee of Bellin Health's FastCare business model, it established two retail clinics at Shopko Expresss, a department store with pharmaceutical and optical departments. Customers were still connected to ThedaCare through electronic health records, and FastCare nurse practitioners could bring an in-depth understanding of patients' past health history that was not available at Walgreens. ThedaCare Physicians had out-innovated its commercial disruptors! Shortly thereafter, Walgreens and Walmart closed their clinics. Strategy and innovation had worked hand in hand.

In this chapter, I have discussed framing the strategic issue. Strategic issues are what you believe need to be solved to close the gap between where you are (current state) and where you want to be (ideal state). The development of the ideal state is informed by understanding the unmet needs of customers and the community. It then is defined by management and the board in concise terms. The example I used was how the ThedaCare board developed and articulated the new ideal state. Closing the gap to the ideal state may require more than incremental improvement of an existing process. That's where innovation thinking is needed. Beating Walmart and Walgreens at their own game is a great example. In the next chapter, I will cover the development of hypothetical solutions to your strategic issue. If the answer to the strategic issue is a complete mystery, it has implications for whom you will involve in the solution process and the process they will use. Let's move to the cascade of strategic choices.

Chapter 5

Making Strategic Choices
to Close the Gap

*Strategy is about making choices under
conditions of uncertainty and competition.*

—Roger Martin

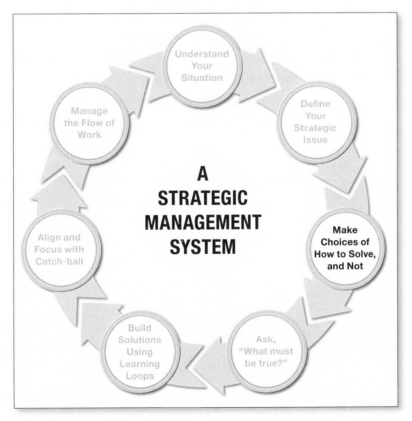

Figure 5.1. A Strategic Management System

D etermining what strategic issue you have to solve is a critical *first* choice. By implication, you also decide that other strategic issues are secondary. In choosing the strategic issue, you are determining what is most important now while you defer and monitor other vital strategic issues.

This is not an easy task. It wasn't for me at ThedaCare and for the many organizations I have dealt with since.

Before we began our lean journey, ThedaCare's senior leadership team would work on many initiatives to accomplish our vision for the organization and to address the strategic issues in front of us. We wanted to be all things to all people and to excel on all fronts at once with the hope of improving our performance in *all* 26 service lines simultaneously. We wanted to grow the volumes at our hospitals, physician offices, and home health and behavioral health units in *all* seven parts of our service area. And we wanted to improve the health of our communities by developing the capability to keep populations healthier, which was a complete change to the organization's business model that could conflict with all the other objectives.

We tried many different techniques throughout the years to see how we could accomplish all of the work we were creating for ourselves. One time we listed all the projects on sticky notes and put them on a large wall. Besides wasting paper, that achieved little. Another time we used the "red dot/green dot" exercise to designate certain initiatives for greater expectations and additional resource allocation (those were green dots) and other initiatives to keep meeting current expectations with limited resource allocation (red dots). Any agreement we would achieve during these meetings would quickly fade, and new initiatives would creep onto the plate almost immediately.

Over time, we turned to help from Matthew May. An expert at developing innovative solutions to complex problems, he has adapted Lafley and Martin's cascade of strategic choices to his visual, engaging approach to facilitating strategy formulation and testing.

Lafley and Martin's cascade of strategic choicess (see Figure 5.2) describes the five dimensions of a strategic option. These dimensions cause the participants in a strategy session to formulate explicit hypothetical solutions to close the gap and solve the key strategic issue. This method was developed, tested, and perfected at Proctor & Gamble and led to its superior performance by making choices and focusing on those choices to create unique customer-centered value. At Proctor & Gamble, this way of thinking was nested at every level in the organization.

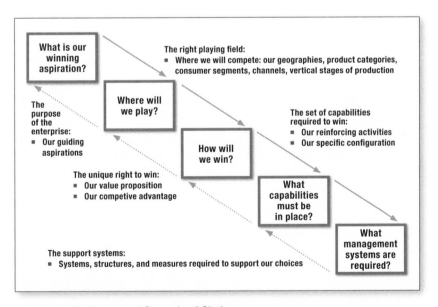

Figure 5.2. An Integrated Cascade of Choices
Reprinted with permission of Harvard Business Review Press.
From Playing to Win *by A.G. Lafley and Roger L. Martin. Boston, MA, 2013, page 15.*

May developed an interactive method for facilitating the development of the Lafley and Martin Playing to Win framework. He uses 24" × 48" canvases to facilitate the diverging/converging discussions in each of the five dimensions of the cascade.

At ThedaCare we learned the method and applied it to our strategic issue. I then used this method to facilitate the Catalysis board retreat. Since 2013, I have experimented with this approach in more than 20 settings, from healthcare to manufacturing, professional services to human agencies. I have found the method effective at engaging professionals in meaningful dialogue that culminates in decisions about what to pursue next and what to defer for later.

The rest of this chapter explains the steps in what appears to be a linear, sequential order. In reality, teams question their thinking in an iterative manner. The cascade of questions becomes a hypothesis as teams continue to go through iterations until they are satisfied they have developed the strategic solution as best as possible until testing starts. With the strategic issue defined, the team can develop hypothetical ways to solve for it. As this thinking becomes nested in an organization, it is practiced at any place or level.

A leadership team takes usually two days to complete the full cascade of choices, reverse engineer their own logic, and then choose their experiment or experiments. Prior to the two-day session, participants, who usually number around 15, are required to read both Lafley, Martin, and Riel's article "A Playbook for Strategy" and a market position assessment prepared by the leadership team. I know this takes time, but when we finished at North Memorial, Kevin Croston, who was initially skeptical of this exercice, said, "This was worth it!"

Occasionally, a senior leadership team has wanted me to engage their board in this process. In one day at a board retreat, we discuss only Lafley and Martin's first three questions about winning aspiration, where to win, and how to win. Then we briefly reverse engineer the board's logic, since it will leave key capabilities and management systems and subsequent experiments to the leadership.

At the two-day session, based on the market position assessment, the participants identify a wide range of alternative ways to solve the strategic issue. This is particularly useful when the nature of the problem is complex and the answer is unknown. Individual participants generate multiple where to win/how to win combinations to create the initial framing of alternatives. Next, the participants diverge into teams to brainstorm potential options and settle on two or three with the most potential.

Many mental models can help teams identify alternatives. One I've frequently used where the strategic issue relates to growth is the following:

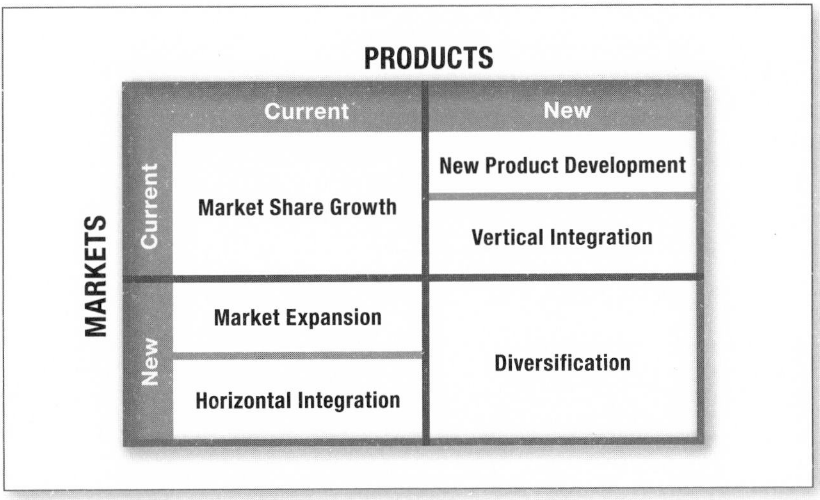

Figure 5.3. Ways to Grow a Business

The next step involves participants breaking into subgroups, with each subgroup exploring one option. For example, at a recent session with a healthcare system, the teams picked three options to examine: one was to spread their current value proposition to a new market segment, one was to develop a new value proposition for current customers, and one was to create a new value proposition that would serve a new customer segment.

For the alternative assigned to them, the subgroup reviews the strategic issue that is common to all groups, examines the option they have been assigned, and begins with a winning aspiration.

Winning Aspiration

The team assigned to a selected strategic option starts by framing what winning looks like with their customers as compared to their competitors. I prompt the discussion with "What will great look like, and how would you know?" It differs from a common vision statement in its specificity about winning with customers against competitors. I also beg the question of "How would you know?" by asking: "Will you be using measures of the classic marketing framework, such as measures of customer awareness for your business or specific service, preference for your organization over your competitors, utilization or volume, market share, or customer loyalty?" I use this question to get the team working together to diverge and then converge on a common perspective.

Where to Win

After answering these questions, the group next identifies *where* the organization must win (Lafley and Martin call this "Where to Play"). Participants must select distinct customer segments, spaces, or channels that the organization must win over its competitors. Just as importantly, they must pick the segments or spaces where it was NOT critical to win at the present time; if you can learn to win in certain spaces, this knowledge can be applied to win in adjacent spaces over time. There can be many possible dimensions or interpretations of where to win: demographic factors such as age, gender, or geographic segments where customers reside; or business-to-business segments; or a platform such as Uber, Google, or Amazon. (Amazon only *started* with books; Uber only *started* with transportation. Both are now talking about entering the healthcare space.)

For me, a helpful mental model when trying to think about this question is a target audience. In this mental model, the center ring is the audience where you must win, the core customer for your value proposition. As you move away from the core, the nearby concentric circles represent audiences that are secondary and tertiary targets. The outer rings are audiences that you do not intend to attract because their preferences and needs are contrary to your value proposition. The center of the target is where you must win; the outer circle is where you choose *not* to appeal to at this point in time.

These are not lifetime decisions. One of the other spaces (or target rings) might become appealing over time. Focus on the target that is most critical to success *now* to solve your strategic issue. You will continue to serve other segments with your current value proposition for the time being. Choose a few segments now to create or enhance your value proposition where you must win.

I call this part of the exercise "where to win" rather than "where to play" because many healthcare professionals during strategy sessions revert to their "all things to all people for the next three to five years" mind-set. They describe every segment they currently serve as equally important and are unwilling to make choices. They want to improve every value proposition at once. The concept of a target audience helps leadership teams become more comfortable discriminating between where to win and where to play.

This mind-set is consistent with lean thinking. When you apply lean to improvement work using PDSA cycles, your first countermeasure is an experiment. Once you are confident that the new countermeasure is working in the model cell, then you spread the solution to the rest of the organization and standardize the process just like concentric rings of a target. The model cell is an inch-wide, mile-deep redesign of an existing care model. This requires redefining the roles and responsibilities of everyone involved in the care delivery value stream. The end result is a completely new process that is patient focused and produces 50%–80% improvements in cost and quality outcomes.

ThedaCare Physicians, our employed primary care group, understood this process. One particular site, the Kimberly Clinic, embraced experimentation—it liked to try new process improvements to create new customer value—and became the model cell. Once the clinic proved that the new outpatient care model delivered better cost and quality outcomes, ThedaCare Physicians spread the solution to its other 23 sites in three phases rather than all at once.

The change was so great that leaders found that dividing the spread into three separate learning modules was necessary so as not to overwhelm the staff and physicians. For example, one of the major changes was having blood tests turned around in 15 minutes in the outpatient clinic. This meant that the medical assistants had to learn how to draw blood. The lab technicians had to completely change their work flow so that the results could be updated in the electronic health records system before a patient left the clinic. But this was a very important change because it allowed the physicians to have all the results and make the necessary adjustments in therapy at the time of the visit rather than trying to catch up with a patient later through phone calls and email.

After you have made discrete choices of where to win for now, the next step in developing your hypothesis is to figure out *how* to win in that space.

How to Win

The combination of attributes that create competitive advantage is externally facing since these attributes are what the customer will describe about you, based on his or her experience in dealing with you. Do you really have:

- Higher quality?
- Better service?
- More access?
- More reliability?
- A more personal experience?
- Faster delivery or throughput?
- More knowledgeable providers?
- More innovation?
- A better price?

It won't matter what you *say*; it will only matter what the customer *experiences*. The customer will determine whether you are differentiated from competitors in a way that is relevant and meaningful to him or her.

After years of a strategy of being all things to all people, healthcare organizations have difficulty realizing they have very few points of relevant differentiation. I have found that leadership teams tend to list *all* the above factors when I ask them what makes them unique. Often, they will say, "We will provide a better value by being higher quality and lower cost." While that aspiration is noble, they are not making choices of how they will be viewed as unique by their target customers by appealing to the distinct needs of that target segment.

Healthcare organizations abhor the idea of cost leadership because they confuse it with price leadership, and they don't believe that competing on price is consistent with their brand image of excellence. Most think they are of higher quality than their competitors even if there is little evidence to support this contention. Healthcare organizations thus frequently choose a strategy of differentiation focus but are not producing relevant differentiation. They become caught in a commodity trap that eventually leads to new entrants.

Organizations can learn from new entrants into the healthcare space that know how to choose segments and develop unique value propositions. For example, SmartChoice MRI is a Wisconsin-based provider of freestanding imaging services that competes on faster access, a better experience, and price leadership. It doesn't try to compete in all segments and spaces, only in certain geographies, certain imaging modalities, and certain patient types. Its leadership team makes conscious choices of where and how it will compete and not compete. In three years, it has grown to 15 locations in three states.

Healthcare systems are compelled to play in many spaces. But they can choose the few in which they must win at a given time and develop sources of competitive advantage in those spaces. When identifying these sources of competitive advantage, you must discriminate between sources of competitive advantage that are important to customers and achievable and ones that are not relevant. Be explicit about the attributes where you match competitors and those where you may lag behind them.

The target audience, segment, or space in which you want to win will be looking for certain characteristics. These are the potential sources of your competitive advantage. Once you have hypothesized what they are, based on your deepest customer insights, turn your attention to the capabilities you need to create that competitive advantage.

Key Capabilities and Management Systems

Teams frequently run into confusion between how to win and key capabilities. How to win is the externally facing dimensions of competitive advantage that customers would say about you. Key capabilities are internally facing; they are what you must consistently do at the highest level to create a competitive advantage. They require the organization to redesign its processes to own that key capability.

Focus only on *key* capabilities. It will help if you articulate capabilities needed to just "play to play," so you can differentiate them with those that are necessary to win. Since you are engineering a process-based solution, competitive advantage is *how* you exploit that capability.

For example, a key capability for an organization that wants to become a population health manager might be customer relationship management. Healthcare systems have a long tradition of transactional customer relationships. Compared to retail providers, healthcare organizations have not leveraged technology to gain insights into their target customer segments and to develop long-standing relationships with them. After treatment ends, hospitals wait until patients return.

This is a legacy of the fee-for-service, volume-based business model. Since population health managers proactively communicate new value propositions to customers, healthcare organizations have to make a complete cultural shift in how they view patients.

Walgreens has no such problem. It accumulates information on its customers and uses it to offer new value propositions to them. Senior leadership teams often react to this new direction as an invasion of patients' privacy. And a host of privacy laws do make this new direction layered with difficulties. Despite these concerns, healthcare organizations need to determine key capabilities in a changing competitive environment.

Management systems are needed to support the key capabilities. Population health managers, for example, require the key capability of managing deep, long-term customer insights and a customer relationship management system that will enable them to cultivate these relationships over time better than their competitors can.

Many healthcare systems, particularly those focused on lean, such as those in the Catalysis Healthcare Value Network, are investing in the development of their employees. For them, their process improvement system is critical to improving their capability to learn faster than competitors.

Another useful management system is unit-based cost accounting. Often lacking in healthcare organizations, this system helps you understand your true cost of doing business and the proposed process changes needed to create new value propositions.

When you have finished identifying the key capabilities and management systems that will help in decision making, you have completed the first iteration of your hypothesis. More iterations are needed before you proceed. So taking a look backward to your entire logic at this point can be helpful.

It is important to iterate your logic on the "where to win" and "how to win" combination. You need to be crystal clear about your hypothesis regarding sources of competitive advantage and segments in which you must win. In addition, you need to ask this question regarding key capabilities: Have I identified the systems necessary to support the competencies I must possess?

Teams need to iterate their way back as they move from one step to another. By the end of the cascade, when teams report their hypothesis, they should describe their conclusions in words similar to these: "Our hypothesis is: if we invest in these systems to support these key capabilities, we will create these sources of competitive advantage in these chosen spaces where we must win, which will enable us to hit our winning aspiration and solve our strategic issue."

The tighter, the better; the more focused, the better. The more you can articulate what it is—and, just as importantly, what it is not—the better.

Each participating team develops alternative ways to solve the strategic issue they have articulated. There might be many hypotheses advanced. Often, a convergence appears among several groups, and a new hypothesis emerges.

Let's now move from workshops to real-world examples.

At ThedaCare, we had decided that our core strategic issue was the opportunity to develop differentiation in the marketplace by helping a specific target audience—a person with serious health issues whom we called Lori—navigate a complex system of care. We conceptualized

Lori as being in her mid-40s with a husband, two children, and two aging parents.

When we began to work on the strategy of helping Lori, we designated four service lines to explore: cardiovascular, orthopedics, cancer, and spine. These were four of our largest service lines, encompassing two-thirds of our organization. This meant we were going to completely change the ThedaCare business model from a vertical to a horizontal orientation all at once. As you might expect, we did not get very far.

Fortunately, we had established a team for this breakthrough initiative, led by Kathryn Correia, then president of our two largest hospitals, Appleton Medical Center and Theda Clark Medical Center, and Greg Long, MD, the chief medical officer for the system. They looked at the struggles we were having in all four service lines to identify the biggest barriers to and enablers of change.

These learnings became inputs into our first playing-to-win session. We had to make choices. Even with expert outside facilitation, we struggled. We continued to describe ourselves as all things to all people. We wanted to win in every space, with every possible source of competitive advantage all at once. That would require us to have every possible capability supported by every conceivable management system.

However, we persevered and kept applying this same framework. We learned that you must make choices about where to win. If you win in this space, then you can stabilize and standardize and afterward figure out where to win next. As we create breakthroughs in selected spaces, continuous daily improvement is the expectation for others. Focus on the critical few now, and defer others for later until you can get the critical work done.

Eventually, we determined that there were two spaces in which we needed to win (where to win). One was helping Lori with her cancer journey. We had expectations for all service lines for daily continuous improvement, but we needed the pioneering breakthrough work to occur in cancer first. We chose cancer because we thought it had the biggest opportunity to create differentiation in the market.

The other space in which we wanted to win was with the sickest 5% of our patients in the outpatient setting (ThedaCare Physicians). These patients were consuming, on average, $80,000 per year by using the healthcare system constantly, e.g., going to a doctor, calling a doctor, going to the emergency room, etc. Despite all this care, these patients were not getting better.

For each of these two where-to-win spaces, we determined what winning looked like and how we would know (winning aspiration). We decided where we wanted to start winning:

- For cancer patients, it was those with a diagnosis of breast cancer.

- For the sickest 5% of outpatients, it would be in one urban clinic and in one rural clinic where we had many chronically ill patients and significant problems with access to their provider.

We hypothesized how to win (competitive advantage) in each of the chosen spaces:

- For cancer, it was "speed" to diagnosis and treatment and "peace of mind" through improved communication (a better experience).

- For the sickest 5%, it would be how we redesigned the interactions of the care delivery team (and the

team itself) to engage patients in their own care
delivery experience (patient co-creation of value).

As we began our work, we realized our systems were built to support one-time transactional relationships, not the deep customer insights and interactions required to deliver a better patient experience. We recognized that we did not possess the capability and management system for innovation, so we needed to acquire it.

The result of this is that we became collectively better focused on our strategic initiatives, which, in combination with our continuous daily improvement and big rocks, moved us toward our next target state.

I continued to experiment with this approach with other organizations. By this time, John Toussaint was heading up the ThedaCare Center for Healthcare Value, later renamed Catalysis. John and I would periodically check in and discuss what we were seeing on our lean journey. At one particular meeting, I described to John how I thought the cascade of choices was helping ThedaCare make better strategic decisions while staying focused on them. John saw an opportunity to apply this method to his new organization. He and his board had concluded that their original strategy had reached a point of maturity. Now they needed to ask themselves fundamental questions of strategic intent—where to go and how to get there.

As I said previously, despite a very good start for Catalysis, the organization felt it was not transforming the healthcare system fast enough. The Catalysis definition of transformation is an organization that is redesigning care around a patient, allowing the organization's results to be made public, and entering into payment contracts that reward the organization for delivering better customer value.

John put together a market position assessment (current state) that framed a couple of strategic alternatives:

- Go big and broad and compete with consulting companies
- Go narrow with a handful of organizations where the CEOs would commit to the transformation journey

We engaged his board in the playing-to-win method, and they ultimately chose the second option.

North Memorial in Minneapolis provides another example. It solved three key strategic issues by developing hypothetical solutions to address the following questions:

- Could it develop radical new care delivery for its target population?
- Could it maximize the services between its two hospitals in a way that patients and physicians would respond to positively?
- Could it learn how to contract with insurers to take performance risk for managing certain population health segments?

These experiences confirmed what I had learned at ThedaCare. Despite many historic and organizational obstacles, hospital leaders can make choices, come to shared strategic conclusions, generate a hypothesis, and start to experiment with changes. Now that you have made choices, it's time to determine how to test these choices through a process of rapid experimentation.

Chapter 6

Strategy Deployment through Rapid Experimentation

For even the very wise cannot see all ends.
—J.R.R. Tolkien

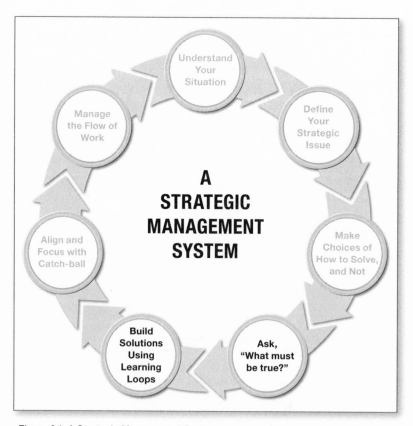

Figure 6.1. A Strategic Management System

The question "What must be true?" is the starting point for strategy deployment. Your hypothesis is based on assumptions you are making about your customers' adoption of your value proposition, your competitors' behavior and response, your own ability to execute on what you intend, and the structure of the industry in which you compete.

Participants question their own logic more effectively and completely when faced with the question "What must be true?" When asked to "list their assumptions," they tend to reply with what they already know rather than search for the most important and unknown answers to important questions. This occurs because people's assumptions are ingrained in their thinking and they tend to list known things for the sake of ease and to avoid the risk of looking uncertain.

Lafley and Martin's strategy logic flow found that a way to break these patterned responses is to ask questions of what must be true about your hypothesis:

- What do your end customers value?

- What do your channels truly value?

- What are your capabilities versus those of your competitors?

- What is your cost structure versus that of your competitors?

- How will your competitors react?

- What is the structure of your industry?

- What is the attractiveness of the segments you have chosen?

As they discuss these questions, teams should brainstorm all the things that must come true for their hypothesis to work. Then they should identify the most critical, unknown assumptions they have about their hypothesis.

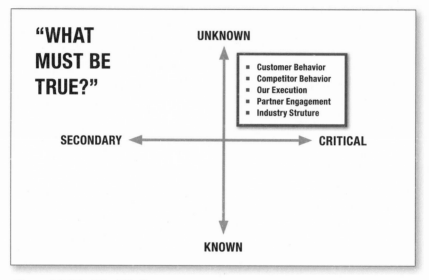

"WHAT MUST BE TRUE?"

UNKNOWN

- Customer Behavior
- Competitor Behavior
- Our Execution
- Partner Engagement
- Industry Struture

SECONDARY ⟷ CRITICAL

KNOWN

Figure 6.2. What Must Be True

Think of all the assumptions you are making as independent variables in a formula. "Critical" means that the outcome of the hypothesis (the dependent variable) is *very* dependent on the answer to this question. "Unknown" means that you do not know the answer to this question. You may have a hunch, or an informed guess, about some of the other assumptions, but the answer to this question is a mystery.

Identifying your most critical and unknown assumptions points you toward where you need to start your experimentation. Often, the most critical and unknown assumptions are in the new value you intend to create and whether customers will respond to that value proposition the way you hope. You must determine what the customer values. You must begin experimenting in a way that ascertains, as quickly and cheaply as possible, whether you are solving a need. As Ted Toussaint, at Atrius Health in Boston, said, "There is no greater waste in the product development process than developing something no one wants to use."

Another useful method is the build-measure-learn feedback loop developed by Eric Ries and inspired by the work of Steve Blank. Based on your customer insight, build a minimal prototype, introduce it, and measure the response; reflect on what you learned; and then determine whether you should continue. The objective is to minimize the total time through the loop. This process starts with leap-of-faith assumptions, which is similar to the critical/unknown assumption described above. Once you know your leap-of-faith assumptions, you must enter the build phase as quickly as possible with a minimum viable product. This version of the product enables a full turn of the build-measure-learn loop with little effort and the least amount of development time.

This approach is consistent with design thinking, where ethnographic approaches provide deep insights into customers' latent and emerging needs. It then introduces a new idea, a prototype, and observes how customers respond. Based on their responses, a design engineer decides whether to pivot or persevere by adding features that customers appear to value.

I have also seen the term "pretotyping" used, rather than "prototyping." The purpose of that term is to get you to think fast and cheap, without overbuilding the initial solution.

Remember my question to the rural hospital CEO: "Is there a way you can test your biggest assumption quickly and cheaply?" Renting another transportation service was his minimum viable product.

A visual method taught to me by Matthew May has been of great aid to me in helping teams learn how to rapidly experiment. It utilizes the same 24" × 48" wall canvas that he developed to facilitate the cascade of strategic choices to form a hypothetical solution. Here a team takes their most critical and unknown assumption and asks: How might we test this assumption in the fastest, least expensive manner? Once the first experiment is run and the learning occurs, the team decides to pivot or persevere.

"Persevering" implies that the experiment seemed to confirm this part of the hypothesis and that the minimum viable product has potential for value creation. It also means running additional experiments, using the next order of critical/unknown assumptions, to build out the solution using additional learning loops.

"Pivot" implies that this experiment did not confirm the original hypothesis for value creation. It doesn't mean the hypothesis is necessarily wrong. Maybe another experiment will confirm it. Pivoting does not mean the experiment was a failure. Rather, it is the basis for team learning. This is a crucial shift in a person's mind-set, which means that he or she is embracing innovation. You need to build a culture of experimentation where participants realize that failure is a necessary part of learning.

Let me provide an example. Homeless Connections is a local emergency shelter that is part of a 28-agency community ecosystem whose mission is to prevent families from being out on the street. If a family is at risk, the ecosystem tries to get them stabilized and then returned to their own home as soon as possible. They call this ideal state "functional zero." Using this strategic management system, Homeless Connections identified its key strategic issue: the temporary housing is always full and there is a waiting list of 70 families. Rather than rushing to build additional housing units, the organization focused on the throughput of its ecosystem. Through their application of lean thinking, they knew these families could be classified as having lower needs, medium needs, and higher needs. The Homeless Connections leadership team became convinced that if the ecosystem was more effective, families with lower needs could be diverted into supporting agencies before they needed emergency shelter, therefore significantly reducing the waiting list.

The leadership team then identified optional hypothetical solutions and used the cascade of strategic choices to flesh out their hypotheses. They found that their current process for evaluating family needs occurred when the family arrived at the shelter. They asked: What if we moved the evaluation process further upstream, when a family is identified and put on the waiting list? Then they formed their hypothesis: Might the evaluation process result in a referral to other agencies in the ecosystem that would help the low-needs family return to functional zero without ever needing to go into the shelter?

After this step they posed this question: "What must be true?" The leadership team focused on their most critical and unknown assumptions. At the top of the list was: Could they could find an effective and efficient evaluation tool that would result in appropriate early referral into the ecosystem? The team's first inclination was to do more market research, which would take more time and resources. Instead, they ran a fast and cheap experiment where a caseworker would choose a few families on the waiting list and test the effectiveness of an evaluation tool.

Their first experiment did not prove that hypothesis. The evaluation tool did not provide enough information. They then pivoted onto another evaluation tool they were familiar with and tested it. They found it too lengthy. Now they are testing an evaluation tool that seems to be meeting the requirements.

I attended their most recent board meeting, where they described their experience with the process. They were enthusiastic that they were focusing on the right things, learning rapidly, and making progress. Because of their renewed focus, they freed up the capacity to begin another set of experiments on another part of the value stream that could potentially contribute to functional zero. They are using lean learning loops to experiment their way to a new target state. When they stabilize that new process, they will again look at the ideal state of functional zero and identify a new hypothesis as a way to get closer.

Strategy deployment is a management process that aligns—both vertically and horizontally—an organization's functions and activities with its strategic objectives. A specific plan is developed with precise goals, actions, time lines, responsibilities, and measures. But an integral step to getting there is the process of *rapid* experimentation to prove a hypothesis true or false. A succession of lean learning loops builds out a solution by testing critical, unknown assumptions in a disciplined, methodical manner. Once it is understood what experiments worked, the overall plan can be developed.

At ThedaCare, one of the breakthrough initiatives we deployed from our strategic plan was called care team design. This initiative targeted the sickest 5% of ThedaCare Physicians' chronic care patients that we described earlier. Our hypothesis was that we could re-deploy ThedaCare Physicians' care team for this targeted segment of patients to improve their health, enhance their patient experience, and save their insurance company money simultaneously.

Before ThedaCare set up a separate team to deploy this hypothesis, months of ethnographic research was done. There was a wall in the Innovation Center at ThedaCare that captured the year-long journey of two of these chronically ill patients. The journey was full of poor hand-offs between specialists and primary care physicians, multiple emergency room visits, social service interventions, etc. It was a visual picture of the mess. This work led to the formation of a team that included a full-time medical director and seven other team members. The experimentation started in only two of the 23 ThedaCare Physicians sites, one urban and one rural. They began with 100 of the group's 250,000 patients, then gradually expanded 100 patients at a time. This team established a rigorous process of rapid experimentation by trying a new intervention every week, starting with a minimum viable product, and then determining when to pivot or persevere in their build-out. Some interventions occurred in the office by organizing team members differently, some were in the patient's home, and some were different combinations of virtual health services.

ThedaCare Physicians used this strategy deployment process to improve patient safety, patient health outcomes, and increased patient and employee satisfaction. Unfortunately, the program wasn't affordable under a volume-based, fee-for-service reimbursement system. That became the next frontier. We now asked: Could we move the market to one that would reward this better value by changing the nature of reimbursement?

Another good example of strategy deployment through rapid experimentation is Atrius Health, one of the nation's most innovative systems. Formed in 2004, it is the largest independent physician-led healthcare organization in the Northeast. With 29 clinical locations, 50 specialties, and 875 physicians, it treats more than 675,000 adult and pediatric patients in eastern and central Massachusetts.

In 2009, Atrius Health signed onto the Blue Cross Blue Shield of Massachusetts Alternative Quality Contract (AQC) as one of the first models of an accountable care organization (ACO). It also participated in the Centers for Medicare & Medicaid Service's Pioneer ACO program. By 2015, the quality scores of Atrius Health's Pioneer ACO were the highest among the Pioneer ACOs in Massachusetts and the third highest nationally among Pioneer ACOs. Its primary care practices have received the highest possible national accreditation as Level 3.

From its beginnings, Atrius was concerned with innovation. For years, it focused on standardizing processes, removing waste, and improving efficiency using activities employing lean. The original approach was dubbed "Care Model Improvement." Then Atrius's leaders decided even bigger breakthroughs might be possible. The goal became to replace existing processes using "Care Model Innovation." To achieve this, Dr. Karen DaSilva was named vice president of innovation and helped establish the Atrius Health Innovation Center. Her charge was to create a core innovation team and process while building an innovation culture across the organization.

One of the center's first initiatives was the Care in Place project, which focused on better serving patients over 65 years old. When a patient that age calls Atrius with urgent health problems but is unable come in to the office, a visiting nurse is dispatched to his or her home within two hours. The nurse has phone access to a geriatric care-trained nurse practitioner who, based on the nurse's assessment, can order tests (including in-home imaging), place prescriptions, and make treatment decisions. Without this service, almost 50% of the patients would have been sent to the emergency room. The program is a win/win/win: patients achieve their goals of staying in their homes, high-quality medical care is given, and the costs are reduced by avoiding unnecessary hospitalization.

Care in Place was the result of a process to generate in-depth information about customers. Dr. DaSilva said that she and her team "had to keep up with the disruption in the healthcare field and had to learn through researching the customers' unmet needs."

The Innovation Center team held a series of town halls, provider focus groups, and customer interviews. In these settings, patients expressed intense feelings about high costs, lack of access to care, staying in their homes, and being treated as people. This information helped Atrius understand what was lacking in the care. As Ted Toussaint says, "Most of what we were finding we had heard before, but seeing everything together in one room was visually powerful." In his words, it provided an "empathy transfer." In one particularly powerful quote, one of the patients said, "I didn't think I was elderly until I went to the hospital. I would rather die than go back." For Ted it was a shock. "Things were not working as we thought. This process helped us examine our own biases and our own information filters. It was 'emotional content' and helped us have an emotional understanding of the customer's needs." Ted says this "empathy transfer" motivated him and others on the team to push much harder to change the larger organization.

In addition, the Innovation Center generated data about the clinical experience by repeatedly meeting with more than 60 different workgroups, leaders, departments, tech vendors, etc. Out of this effort came new insights. For example, one of the Innovation Center's physicians conducted a chart review of 400 ER visits. His conclusion was that nearly 50% of those patients sent to the ER did not need that level of care.

Dr. DaSilva said that from all the feedback and patient stories, they built a grid that demonstrated how frequently the patients' needs occurred. They then took the major themes and broke them down by frequency of occurrence and impact. The top priority became the most frequently unmet needs with the highest impact. There were 50 different categories of needs. On a board she and her team placed 1,200 sticky notes and used them to think through categories. They next took the notes and put 40–50 of them into buckets. Out of this they created 10 priority areas and projects that would impact the problems identified by customers. One became Care in Place.

The Care in Place team tested different designs very quickly, guided by the idea of prototyping. The Atrius leaders firmly believed it was a critical component of innovation. Prototyping care models requires quick access to care locations, medical supplies, IT systems, new medical devices and technology, and face time with different providers. The innovation and operations teams must work together and negotiate the use of these resources.

Ted and Karen co-authored an article with John Toussaint in *Harvard Business Review* entitled "How Atrius Health Is Making the Shift from Volume to Value" in which they detail the journey of the Care in Place team. What I found most inspirational was how they involved Atrius's senior leadership team, the Innovation Center leaders, and the Care in Place team in the PDSA thinking that developed innovative solutions for their patients. They exemplified how you can engage all levels in the organization in the learning cycle with visual management and standard work.

The common theme with these examples is that senior teams need to focus on a clear hypothesis and then accelerate their learning through rapid experimentation.

When we first tried this approach at ThedaCare, we found we were giving insufficient direction. We followed up by having the senior leadership team complete the background, current state, and problem or opportunity they saw for each breakthrough initiative. This helped establish clarity about what we expected from the experimentation team in terms of deliverables and timeframes. We did not tell them what to do or how to do it. Rather, we set the expectation that they would develop the new standard process to achieve a new level of performance with a timeframe. For any strategic breakthrough initiative, we assigned at least one senior leader and often paired him or her with a leader-in-training. We were explicit about the objectives, the timeframes, the resources they could expect, and the boundaries and restraints on them. They would recruit team members.

In this chapter you have learned how to expand on the strategic choices of new, differentiating processes that you believe are critical to becoming unique in the eyes of your customers. Knowing that these proposed solutions are hypotheses, you have learned to ask yourself, "What must be true?" and have organized teams to build out these solutions through rapid experimentation. Now, you must align this work with those in the organization who are already busy with their everyday work, applying continuous daily improvement to that work and implementing big rocks. The key to doing this is catch-ball, the subject of the next chapter.

Chapter **7**

The Technical and Human
Sides of Catch-Ball

*[Dialogue] is not something you **do to** another
person. It is something you **do with** people.*
—William Isaacs
Dialogue and the Art of Thinking Together

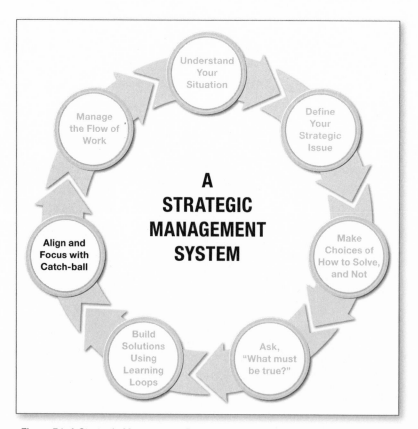

Figure 7.1. A Strategic Management System

When leadership teams first go through the cascade of strategic choices and then identify their initial experiments, they often feel enthused and focused. But it's very easy to slip back into their old mental model and lose the momentum they have built by including all levels of the organization in understanding the current situation and participating in solving problems and opportunities.

Four critical enablers keep their momentum going. The first is a team's ability to apply lean learning loops repeatedly in developing a proposed solution, a topic covered in the previous chapter. The second key enabler is using productive dialogue—the lean term is "catch-ball"—to align the work horizontally and vertically throughout an organization. A third enabler is how a senior leadership team studies and adjusts strategy deployment to help other teams with their decisions to pivot or persevere. And the last enabler is the process by which that team manages all work-in-process—the combination of breakthrough initiatives and big rocks that consumes an organization's discretionary resources. (These last two are the subject of chapter 8.)

Jason Douglas, the CEO of Memorial Medical Center in Ashland, Wisconsin, and Tim Gillingsrud, CEO of Hayward Area Medical Center in Haywood, Wisconsin, lead two organizations bonded by an affiliation. They work together to improve the quality of healthcare in northwest Wisconsin through strategic initiatives. When their combined senior leadership teams completed their first iteration of the cascade of choices, they had involved each hospital's strategic planning committee and the board of each hospital. They also conducted a joint retreat of both hospitals' strategic planning committees; then they had a joint manager retreat of both organizations and culminated with a joint board retreat of the two hospitals. Such significant input supported Jason's and Tim's belief that they had developed a good hypothesis.

They concluded that their previous strategy of adding more services would be insufficient unless they addressed their key strategic issue: urban hospitals and insurance companies outside their immediate service area owned most of the channels to those services. As demand for healthcare services slowed throughout the entire region, those organizations steered patients away from local providers in Ashland and Hayward toward the urban hospitals. With this reality in mind, Jason and Tim worked with their leadership teams to develop a hypothetical solution: expand direct relationships with patients in a way that complemented their local physicians rather than competed with them. They decided on a handful of experiments to see whether this hypothesis would work in the marketplace. One initiative involved managers and employees of the emergency rooms in developing urgent-care services that would complement the local primary care physicians. Another initiative involved the managers and employees of the obstetrical service in developing longer and deeper relationships with mothers and their children before and after hospital delivery.

Jason and Tim had spent a number of months working with leadership teams, committees, and boards of trustees to develop a collective understanding of their current problem, support for their hypothetical solution, and assistance for their proposed experiments to alleviate the problem.

At the same time, they realized they needed meaningful conversations with managers throughout the organization to obtain complete buy-in. Otherwise, they might overburden professionals and staff who already had a full plate of patient care. In addition, many were participating in such big-rock projects as electronic health record adoption, revenue cycle improvement, and facilities renovations. They needed to be respectful of the burden already placed on their managers and employees. It was time for catch-ball.

What is catch-ball? Remember when you were a kid and a friend came over to your house with a ball glove? You grabbed yours and went outside, sometimes to a backyard or to a ball field. You would throw the ball back and forth for hours. You learned quickly that if you did not throw the ball in a manner in which the other person could catch it, and vice versa, the game wasn't much fun. Played together, both you and your friend got better.

With that memory in mind, catch-ball in lean thinking is a continuous, ongoing process of identifying priorities, making decisions, discussing implications, and reallocating resources. Playing catch-ball ensures that everyone who should give input does. And it makes certain that everyone is committed to doing what everyone agreed to.

Regardless of who initiates a project (although it's most commonly a manager), that person articulates the purpose, objectives, ideas, and concerns and then throws these elements to others for feedback, support, and action. The catch-ball process begins when a manager assembles a core implementation team and identifies an area to improve.

How did Jason and Tim proceed with their initiative? There are two dimensions to catch-ball. One is mechanical, involving the methodological process by which these discussions happen. These tools I introduce here. The other is interpersonal, involving mental models and tools, which are covered later in this chapter.

I know more about the mechanical side—the systems and tools for visual management of the process. I learned those elements at ThedaCare. We did this aspect of strategy deployment very well. In the course of a year, beginning in January and concluding in March, we would initiate a systematic process for involving as many people as possible in the organization to produce an annual market position assessment. We then would discuss the key strategic issues identified in the assessment by April and May. Next, we would present a draft strategic plan with strategic initiatives to the board in June and finalize the expectations for those initiatives for board approval in August.

Where we fell down, however, was our assumption that catch-ball would occur among senior leaders and their direct reports and between team leaders and eventually trickle down to staff. This was a very bad assumption, one that smacked of hubris and an inadequate understanding of the complexity of involving people in changes that were affecting them. Inevitably, a wave of feedback indicated that we were overburdening the staff and that they didn't understand the strategic plan and their role in it.

Upon reflection, I learned that leaders must translate strategic intent to their direct reports in clear, unambiguous language and in a respectful manner but also allow for feedback to come back up the organizational structure. This unlocks direct reports' creativity. What we should have done was propose a target condition for them to achieve and then encourage them to develop a process that would help them consistently hit that target. We should not have told them what to do and how to do it; rather, we should have given them the task and let them try to accomplish it with our assistance. I needed to understand much more about the human side of change, which I will get to shortly.

What I found useful in helping organizational leaders with strategic management was a tool called the X-matrix. It supports dialogue between people, and it helps develop and implement strategic plans across an organization. The X-matrix also supports ownership of and accountability for plans at all levels while encouraging organizational learning, faster course corrections, and cross-departmental coordination.

Some people share my enthusiasm for the X-matrix, while others don't. Problems arise, I believe, when it is a standalone tool rather than part of a system. Some X-matrices are too complicated. At ThedaCare, a very confusing form created a roadblock to change until we simplified it.

The stripped-down tool that we used at ThedaCare had four dimensions:

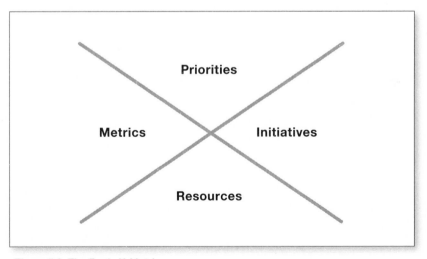

Figure 7.2. The Basic X-Matrix

At the 9:00 position, on the left side, are the metrics—the driver numbers—the organization is trying to achieve. Your key performance indicators (KPIs) are often derived from your True North metrics. Place your KPIs here. Next, at the 12:00 position, on the top, are key breakthrough priorities—the results of the strategic choices you have made that propel those results. At the 3:00 position, on the right side, are initiatives, the current experiments that you believe will accomplish your priorities. At the 6:00 position, on the bottom, are resources required to complete those initiatives. This includes your employees, departments, and operating units whose energy you are going to consume.

An effective X-matrix enables two parties to have a dialogue about the work they are proposing to initiate now and the resources they think must be deployed to it. In my experience, the most crucial catch-ball discussions are focused on the resources necessary to accomplish all the work. The absence of resources on an X-matrix does not help this critical discussion.

When a senior leadership team identifies their hypothesis, breakthrough initiatives, driver numbers, and experiments, they place these inputs at the appropriate position on their X-matrix, which I call the Level-1 X-matrix, the senior leadership level.

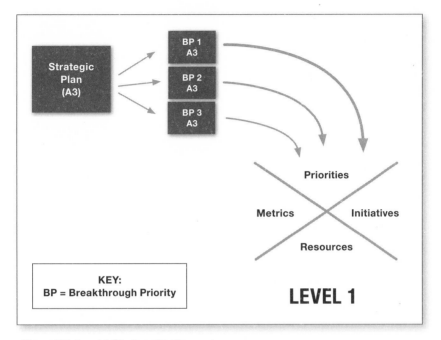

Figure 7.3. Level 1 Strategy Deployment

Leaders should put the category of big rocks at the 12:00 position and list each of the big rocks at the 3:00 position. This helps them see all the critical, cross–organizational priorities they are deploying.

At next level of the organization (Level 2), an operating unit or functional unit should have its own X-matrix that reflects its priorities. Such priorities are a combination of breakthrough strategy deployment initiatives and big rocks from the 3:00 position of the senior leadership's Level 1 X-matrix and its own business plan for that operating or functional unit.

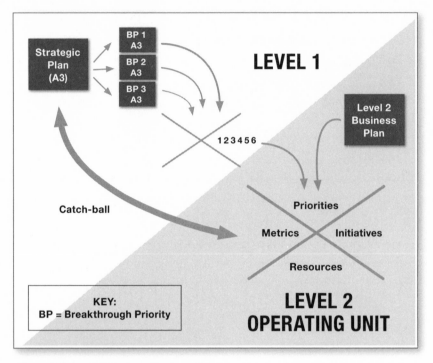

Figure 7.4. Level 2 Strategy Deployment

Once completed, all parties should discuss this question: What priorities have precedence over what other work? Ultimately, the senior leadership team has the final say in setting precedence. While this implies a top-down management approach, a particular challenge in a professional organization like a healthcare system, the key is how to engage people in a respectful dialogue so that all viewpoints are heard and considered.

Some of ThedaCare's most innovative work was not deployed directly from the senior leadership team's strategic plan and X-matrix. It came from the openness and dialogue that the X-matrix supports. The Collaborative Care initiative that redesigned the inpatient care process was derived from the combined Appleton Medical Center and Theda Clark Medical Center business plan. The same was true for ThedaCare Physicians' New Delivery Model that produced breakthrough results in primary care delivery. That initiative also came from their business plan.

The ThedaCare strategic plan called on the system to develop their better care process *across* the operating units, not within them. Business plans of the operating or functional units were full of process improvement initiatives within their unit. Use of the X-matrix at each organizational level enabled us to discuss and resolve our differing perspectives over priorities. We then adjusted the work so that we could accomplish the enterprise-level and operating unit–level priorities that we agreed on. Work going on horizontally and vertically throughout the system was reconciled through catch-ball.

The ThedaCare information technology (IT) functional support unit provides a great example of catch-ball at its best. IT had its own X-matrix that reflected priorities that came from above and the priorities of each of our operating units (seven hospitals, primary care, home health, behavioral health, etc.). IT also had its own business plan that reflected its priorities for radically improving the processes for delivering service to the organization. All of this was poured into the 12:00 position of ITs X-matrix. Then IT listed the brand-new initiatives that staff members were being asked to do at the 3:00 position—all *114* of them. Because IT people are very good at project management, particularly estimating resources, they indicated that at the 6:00 position, 20 new staff members and over $20 million in additional consulting funds were needed to accomplish the 114 initiatives. They then threw this information back to the senior leadership team and to the operating units. After absorbing this reality and subsequent discussions, senior leaders reduced the number of initiatives and committed additional personnel and consulting dollars. While IT may have still felt overburdened, the burden had been substantially reduced. Catch-ball in the case of IT was the way senior leaders learned what was really going on.

After 40 years in the health field and more than a decade of being involved with lean, I was still missing a significant area of knowledge in one aspect of catch-ball—its human side.

While at ThedaCare, I personally struggled with the concept of target and means. As a senior leader, I thought I was supposed to delegate the desired target and the *method to get there*, that is, telling someone what to do and how to do it. I had to learn that I had to *ask* someone to help us achieve a new level of performance, and to *build* process capability to consistently hit the higher level of performance. In the words of John Poole, I had to "give them the job and let them try." John had the patience to teach me many things.

I also learned at ThedaCare that when a senior leadership team delegates a breakthrough initiative, they should not put leaders and teams in unwinnable situations. An impossible task will not get many volunteers for the next assignment. In addition, I realized that when coaching team leaders on how to execute an initiative, senior leaders must go where the work is being performed. They must get their hands dirty along with their direct reports.

When you ask someone to help an organization achieve a new level of performance, you are enlisting him or her in determining a new process to consistently hit a new target. This involves creating respectful two-way dialogue and negotiation. If you engage in such effective catch-ball, you will have created a repeatable method that will drive continuous improvement.

This became obvious to me when I observed the behavior of Kathryn Correia and Jenny Redman-Schell, both senior vice presidents at ThedaCare. They would push back against our senior leadership team when they assigned targets to Kathryn and Jenny's operating units that were unrealistic or conflicted with other important work. They intuitively knew how to engage in catch-ball in a respectful, firm manner.

I tried to build on their approach when I worked at the Hayward Area Medical Center and the Memorial Medical Center. CEOs Tim Gillingsrud and Jason Douglas and their senior leaders genuinely wanted the best for their managers and employees. Together they made significant progress—they understood their market situation, identified their strategic issue, engaged stakeholders in making strategic choices, determined their first experiments, and arranged all the work-in-process on an X-matrix.

The one area where Tim and Jason and their team were struggling was engaging in effective catch-ball with their direct reports. They hadn't done this before. They felt awkward and unsure of how to proceed. They kept asking me: What are the steps to this proposed intimate, complex dance?

Frankly, I didn't know. So I started to explore the human side of catch-ball through extensive readings, conversations with colleagues, and, most interestingly, a talk with my son.

On this part of my lean journey, I discovered that when a person or organization is stuck in any situation, senior leaders had to listen and speak effectively, and that was a skill set that could be learned. In *Crucial Conversations*, Kerry Patterson, Joseph Grenny, David Maxfield, Ron McMillan, and Al Switzler delineated the essential elements of crucial conversations. They include:

- **Understanding What Is a Crucial Conversation.** When you face such a conversation, you can avoid it, face it and handle it poorly, or face it and handle it well. Ironically, the more crucial the conversation, the less likely you will handle it well.

- **Understanding the Power of Dialogue.** Dialogue is "the free flow of meaning between two or more people." The more information that is available through dialogue, the better prepared you are to make decisions and get results.

- **Starting with the Heart.** This means examining your personal role in any problem you encounter. You need to ask: Am I striving to look good, win an argument, or achieve some other unhealthy objective?

- **Noticing When Safety Is at Risk.** The sooner you become aware you are not in dialogue, the quicker you can get back to it. Learn to look for signs of silence and violence and for your own style under stress.

- **Making It Safe.** When things go wrong in crucial conversations, your message is the problem. Make the other person know you care about his or her best interests and goals and about him or her. Then he or she will relax and can absorb what you're saying.

- **Staying in Dialogue When You're Angry, Scared, or Hurt.** To stay in dialogue, you must rethink the conclusions you drew and the judgments you made about the other party and allow the possibility that you can return to mutual purpose and mutual respect.

- **Speaking Persuasively, Not Abrasively.** To speak your mind completely, you must express your views in ways that maintain safety while being both confident and humble.

- **Listening When Others Blow Up or Clam Up.** When this happens, move them back to their facts, which can lead to curiosity.

- **Turning Crucial Conversations into Action and Results.** If you don't take action, there will eventually be disappointment and hard feelings. Always agree on when and how follow-up will occur.

With these thoughts in mind about deepening conversational exchanges between participants, I talked with my colleagues at ThedaCare who were experts in organizational development, including Kathy Franklin, Roger Gerard, and Sharon Schumacher— each of whom helped me greatly. I described the problems my clients had with catch-ball and asked them what was driving these reactions. They all agreed that employees feared these conversations because of working in the old command-and-control management paradigm. In addition, some employees didn't believe that other people wanted to truly engage in a give-and-take dialogue.

The final expert who helped me create more effective catch-ball was my son Jesse. He is an officer in the U.S. Marine Corps with a Military Occupational Specialty (MOS) of Logistics. I asked him how the Marines communicate strategic intent from level to level.

He said that much of his officer training was focused on perfecting the process of translating a commander's intent into mission order. Clarity of communication is critical or the consequences can be terrible, literally life or death. Jesse has a role in communicating strategic intent, but he also has a responsibility to advise his senior officer if he thinks there may be a better way to accomplish a mission.

Jesse's responsibilities include planning for a mission (the plan part of PDSA), executing his portion of the mission (do), and participating in study and adjust once a mission is underway. A good example of this was the Marine Corps' initiative to determine how women could be integrated into combat MOSs that were, until then, closed to female Marines. The Corps designed an experiment to test how effective a trained male–female mixed combat unit would be compared to an all-male unit, as well as the physical impact of this work on the women in occupations historically reserved for men. Jesse was involved in the logistical planning to support the experiment so it would not be compromised due to logistical shortfalls. Logistical support, in essence, was to be uninterrupted and held constant in the experiment so that the original hypotheses could be studied without distraction.

Jesse's command received a set of requirements from the units conducting the experiment, then they began their own planning. They coordinated with the experimental unit, and higher-up and adjacent units, to determine the personnel and equipment resources they needed to field in order to support their plan. Ultimately, what they proposed was different and proved to be more effective than what was originally requested. In addition to the identifying resources, they also planned how they would gather, deploy, and return them afterward. As they went into the execution (the "do" phase) of gathering the resources and supplying the experimental unit, they adjusted as unforeseen issues arose and regularly reported the progress to their commander and higher officers (study/adjust).

Jesse's description was amplified in the book *One Bullet Away: The Making of a Marine Officer* by Nathaniel Fick, a former U.S. Marine officer and now CEO of Endgame, a cyber security software company. Fick details the process of receiving and giving orders. When planning an initiative, all command staff members (enlisted and officers) from the battalion level up convene in a room or in the field to hash things out. These meetings follow an agenda in a standardized process. Planning at different levels can happen concurrently. There liaison officers facilitate vertical discussions as horizontal ones take place. Guidance and planning efforts may flow down the chain, but execution is decentralized, and tactical decisions for an operation often come from the bottom up.

Jesse told me that sometimes he can influence the negotiation more than other times. The further down the chain of command, the less a person can influence the overall mission. But each has a responsibility to translate strategic intent and to suggest a better alternative if he or she has one. The phrase used is, you can delegate authority (down) but not responsibility.

I shouldn't have been surprised by this. George Koenigsacker, who originally helped ThedaCare with our adoption of lean, told me that leadership training in the military had many similarities to lean. In lean, the objective is to enable and empower the frontline employee to contribute to the mission and strategy of the organization by seeing and seizing opportunities to improve the process by which he or she creates value. In the military, the objective is to enable the frontline soldier to accomplish the mission under conditions of uncertainty and competition and to live through it. The point of leadership training in both situations is to create conditions in which frontline employees succeed and are inspired to come back for more.

Interactions don't just happen on the front-end planning of an initiative. Officers have to engage in study and adjust discussions *during* an initiative. As in business, strategy is the process of making choices under conditions of uncertainty and competition. Since one cannot predict the future and changing conditions, one must engage in study and adjust reviews to learn quickly and make effective course corrections. To do so, leaders must go to where the work is happening: the front lines. Commanders must assess what happened after an engagement. Battalion-level units and higher levels then are required to complete and submit after action reports (AARs).

I believe the military experience translates very well into business and healthcare systems. For example, Team Rubicon is a company that unites the skills and experiences of military veterans and first responders to rapidly deploy emergency response teams. Their motto is "Disasters are our business. Veterans are our passion." Team Rubicon was started by Marine veterans who saw natural disasters occurring and knew they could help. They provide a quick, thorough response including essential services, medical care, and clean water. As in the military, their planning involves a process of making choices under conditions of uncertainty and competition. They use their knowledge and skills to deploy solutions, using communication and catch-ball to rapidly plan, do, study, and adjust under very challenging circumstances.

Based on all of my explorations, I began to formulate a model of how to conduct catch-ball sessions. I came to learn there are four levels of questions that need to be built into a productive interaction:

1. Objective—understand what is being said and the facts behind it.

2. Reflective—my opportunity to think about what it means to me.

3. Interpretive—my opportunity to think about what it means to the topic.

4. Decisional—where implications and new directions are formed.

The person initiating the dialogue frames it by explaining the situation or context for the discussion. He or she communicates the strategic intent, or the mission; the objective, or the target; and why it is important. He or she is asking the respondent to discover a process, a new standard by which this target can be consistently met going forward. He or she also describes the resources that the respondent can expect to receive, based on what is known so far and any boundaries or constraints on the initiative that are known so far.

The person initiating the dialogue then allows the respondent to ask questions of the initiator in the inquiry phase. These include: What clarifying questions does the respondent have? What are his or her first thoughts or reactions to what he or she has heard? What are his or her feelings based on what he or she has heard? Then the respondent has the opportunity to advocate for his or her initial position by describing his or her opinion based on what he or she has heard so far, the resources he or she thinks he or she needs, how he or she thinks it will impact his or her priorities, and how he or she initially thinks he or she might proceed with the initiative.

Next the respondent throws the ball back to the initiator. The person initiating the dialogue gets his or her turn to ask questions to make sure he or she understands the meaning of the respondent; he or she gets to describe what he or she is thinking and feeling given the new information. He or she then advocates for his or her position.

Through these iterations of hearing each other in a safe, respectful manner, people have the potential to come to a common understanding.

It takes time and patience for participants in healthcare organizations to gain experience and to become comfortable with the process of meaningful catch-ball. We have generations of preconceived notions and experiences to overcome. Margie Hagene, a Catalysis executive coach, suggests that leaders become more comfortable using dialogue in a strategy deployment situation the more they practice it in other situations, such as when coaching direct reports in problem solving.

Now that you have become aware of both the importance and the difficulty of catch-ball, let's move on to some of the challenging aspects of a strategic management system and how to deal with them.

Chapter 8

Managing Focus and
Accelerating Learning

Everything we need to know is on the wall.
—Kevin McNamara
President/CEO, TIDI Products

Figure 8.1. A Strategic Management System

I f you have been following the steps laid out so far, your senior leadership team has used PDSA thinking to engage your organization in a process of understanding your current situation, your ideal state or vision, and your next target state. After doing this, they have chosen the breakthrough initiatives (which are hypotheses) to get to that target state. At this point, they believe that the combination of breakthrough initiatives, operational effectiveness, and nondifferentiating yet important big-rock projects will move your healthcare system closer to True North.

In addition, your senior leaders have asked team leaders and staff to start their initiatives with a minimum viable product and then to build toward a solution through rapid experimentation using lean learning loops. Because such initiatives are new work piled on top of operational effectiveness and big rocks, senior leaders and your teams used catch-ball dialogic techniques to align the resources of operating and functional units in the organization so this important work was started.

The plan portion of the PDSA cycle is now completed, and the do portion has begun. As I said previously, four enablers keep momentum going. The first is the use of lean learning loops described in chapter 6. The second is the effective use of catch-ball covered in chapter 7. This chapter describes the third and fourth enablers—the study and adjust parts of the cycle. Senior leaders now must effectively manage this work-in-process so as to accelerate learning. And they must reprioritize, defer, or deselect current initiatives while identifying and prioritizing new initiatives. This is not easy, but it is critical in maintaining focus and continuing to reduce overburden and accelerate learning.

A visual management system is vital in helping people see and be in control of their work. Using such a system enables teams to clearly view what they are working on and whether they are winning. Team members often want to avoid prioritizing and making decisions. Without an easy way to see the work so discussions can proceed in a respectful manner, organizational efforts bog down and eventually fail.

Many books, webinars, and other learning methods describe the mechanics of setting up visual management systems and how to hold catch-ball discussions where the work is being done.

All such systems include certain key elements. The first is the use of tracking centers at every level in the organization to help frontline employees see how their effort is improving the patient's experience and contributing to the overall effectiveness of their teammates and the organization.

Tracking centers are used at the front line so employees can discuss their customers' pain points and collectively decide how they can initiate experiments to solve them. These centers are gathering spots for employees to participate in daily improvement, understand the big rocks, and know whether they are involved in a strategic breakthrough initiative. The tracking center is used to capture the unit's contribution to the organization's True North metrics. These metrics may include safety, quality, customer satisfaction or delivery of service, employee engagement, and financial performance. For each metric, charts depict whether the unit is meeting its expected level of performance. If not, other charts help the unit determine when, where, and why the problem seems to be occurring.

Tracking centers also include problem-solving reports. These reports are generally on a single sheet of paper and contain the background, current condition, problem statement, target condition, analysis, and countermeasures proposed by staff. At ThedaCare we call these single-sheet reports PDSAs. They are sometimes called an A3, named after the 11" × 17" size of the paper that is used. The reports include the current actions the unit is taking to solve problems, and they depict ideas that the staff has generated to improve current levels of performance. These ideas are placed in a queue to be acted on when capacity opens up (see Figure 8.2).

Figure 8.2. Tracking Center

Each level in the organization has a tracking center. The senior leadership team does also. They use it to observe, at the enterprise level, whether they are on track and winning on important metrics. At ThedaCare, we had a visual management room. One wall contained our tracking center. Another wall displayed our strategy deployment— the progress we were making on our breakthrough initiatives. This wall also showed our PDSAs (A3s) on the breakthrough initiatives we were deploying. A third wall depicted our work-in-process captured by an X-matrix, as well as exhibited new ideas that would enable us to achieve our priorities.

As I said earlier, an X-matrix provides a snapshot of your work-in-process by showing your combination of strategic breakthrough initiatives and big rocks. The snapshot should be appropriate for that operating unit, the functional support area, or the level in the organization. At ThedaCare, we once tried to capture on a single X-matrix all of the projects at every level of the organization. Instantly, we created the world's largest X-matrix. It was confusing and not helpful. On our second try, we had each organizational level, such as an operating or functional unit, create an X-matrix specific to that level, and then we engaged in catch-ball. This X-matrix enabled us to have honest discussions about the timing, sequence, and resource needs for the work we wanted to accomplish.

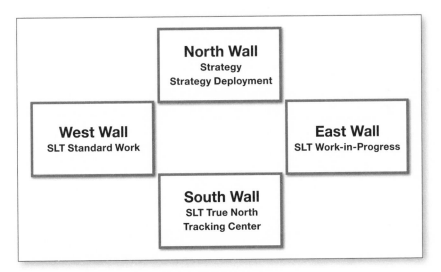

Figure 8.3. Senior Leadership Team Visual Room

As soon as you have completed the plan portion of your strategic plan and have initiated the do portion, new potential initiatives will immediately start coming from inside and outside the organization. This is going to happen in any industry but especially in one as turbulent as healthcare. This is a good thing; you want the new ideas to keep flowing. You want everyone in your organization spotting problems or opportunities and bringing them forward. But it can be overwhelming and can cause you to lose focus if the new ideas are not put in context and managed in a way that maintains your efforts and reduces overburden.

There are a series of steps before a project, either a new strategic breakthrough initiative or a big rock, becomes a work-in-process and can be placed on an X-matrix. These steps include the following:

- The new idea should be captured on an idea board. Often the idea is too new to be clearly defined and needs more information. Sometimes the idea is a heads-up whose time is not yet here but some members are alerting the team that it could be a possibility in the future. The idea board is simple. It contains 3 × 5 sticky notes or index cards that capture what the idea is, the problem or opportunity it may solve (the gap it may close between the current state and the target state), the timeframe in which it should be considered, and who is responsible for bringing the idea forward.

- When there is sufficient information to define the opportunity, an idea should move through the evaluation phase. At ThedaCare we began with a 16-page project proposal. We quickly discovered it overburdened staff and professionals and squashed or bottled up ideas. We moved to using the A3 for the tool to facilitate our PDSA conversations. Using it, a project advocate described the background and current state, the problem or opportunity, the target state, his or her hypothesis for closing the gap (if one existed), and the resources to be used.

- The next phase involved moving those ideas with the highest potential impact to the wait/work board, another lean tool from manufacturing. The wait side of the board contains projects waiting for inputs. The work side contains projects that have all the inputs required for the project. Our senior leadership team maintained a pick chart, a lean tool that depicts the opportunities that had been evaluated arrayed in four quadrants defined by impact and difficulty. Some organizational capacity has to be freed up so the project can move onto the X-matrix and become in-progress.

- The fourth phase involves items currently consuming cross-organizational resources. They are work-in-process and are reflected on the X-matrix. They move from the X-matrix to free up capacity under one of two conditions: the new standard process to create differentiation (strategy) has been developed, is stable and standardized, and has spread; or the big rock project has been completed and the new standard work is applied.

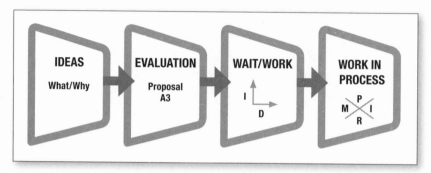

Figure 8.4. Managing the Flow of Work

The visual management room provided a place where we could study the work-in-process, the organization's performance toward its True North goals, and where we could manage the flow of new ideas before they became work-in-process. It was also where we would meet to study, learn, and adjust.

As senior leadership works with the X-matrix and engages in catch-ball, how do they, over time, study and adjust their thinking?

ThedaCare's senior leadership team needed a consistent, methodical process. We met monthly in three-hour sessions devoted to strategy deployment. We would typically have three to five breakthrough initiatives going on at a given time.

For each breakthrough initiative, the team would briefly cover these questions:

- What did we try?
- What did we expect to happen?
- What actually happened?
- What explains the difference?
- What did we learn?

- What are we going to try next?
- Are there any barriers we need to remove?

These are the questions used in the study portion of plan-do-study-adjust. As a senior leadership team answers them, they become collectively nimbler in their strategic thinking and in accelerating learning.

After we covered each of the strategic breakthrough initiatives, we would turn to the big rocks. We did not cover every big rock every time we met. We did have a cadence—a planned time—when we would review each big rock. That cadence would be set according to the major milestones we had for each project. At a minimum, on the third Tuesday of each month, we would study and adjust the strategic breakthrough initiatives, reflect on the big rocks, review our Level 1 X-matrix, and ask ourselves: "Are we deploying the right resources to the right initiatives, accomplishing our priorities, and moving the needle on our driver numbers" so as to reverse engineer our logic flow on the X-matrix?

When the ThedaCare senior leadership team performed a study/adjust for strategic breakthrough initiatives, we would periodically go to the location where the new standard process was being developed to learn how the deployment of this initiative was going and discern whether we could help remove barriers that existed. Later, as we deployed the breakthrough initiative to redesign care for TheadaCare Physicians' most chronically ill patients, we would go to where the team dedicated to that redesign initiative was housed to understand their process and learn from them.

Kevin Croston's team at North Memorial performs monthly reviews of their initiatives. Teams at Memorial Medical Center in Ashland

and Hayward Area Medical Center each have weekly meetings where they study/adjust. This is followed by quarterly meetings of the combined leadership teams where they study/adjust and use X-matrices to see the connection between driver numbers, priorities, initiatives, and resources.

Because the market conditions are so dynamic, the work-in-process needs to be revised constantly as a new issue or opportunity emerges to consume resources. A leadership team needs a method to manage the work-in-process and the influx of new ideas. This method also helps reduce the chance of overburden, prevents stretching resources too thin, and keeps momentum going.

In 2013, ThedaCare was working on our priorities, including a combination of deploying points of differentiation, executing big rocks, and developing a culture that embraced continuous improvement. We thought we had our priorities figured out. Then one day, the CEO of a rural healthcare delivery system that we had been courting for 20 years called and asked to affiliate with us. This was a huge strategic opportunity. This system employed 30 physicians in our expanded service area where we did not have a strong market share. Our answer had to be "Yes!" and we had to act fast.

From three prior affiliations with rural delivery systems, we knew how much work was involved. We even had a value stream that codified the process. We realized resources would be consumed, especially from our information technology, finance, human resources, facilities management, and ThedaCare Physicians functions. In addition, different cultures had to merge, which would raise fears among employees in both organizations.

While acquiring this affiliation was an important strategic imperative, it was NOT part of our strategic differentiation. Our enterprise-wide strategy, our hypothesis, was that meaningful differentiation would be achieved by radically redesigning the *process* by which very ill patients—those with cancer, for example—experienced our cross-operational units. So this affiliation would create a really big rock.

Despite all these concerns, we decided to merge, but we continued redesigning our priorities. We thus had to defer some priorities such as the promise to another rural hospital in our system to construct a new replacement hospital.

Senior leaders must be honest with each other and call out when a new project slides onto the priority list. Because of their focus, information technology followed by finance, human resources, then marketing, in that order, spot such slippage quickly. Frequently, a CEO initiates a new project because he or she is bombarded by key stakeholders inside and outside the organization. The entire leadership team must help manage these situations and declare when they don't make sense.

A senior leadership team must choose which initiatives will be started, which will be continued, and which must stop for a period of time until capacity reopens. These are often unpopular decisions. To ask practitioners to defer their favorite projects is hard before they start; it's even more difficult after the projects are under way. Sometimes there is simply no further capacity, regardless of the number of resources you might throw at an initiative. Sometimes after such decisions are made, practitioners engage in power tactics to get their way. At such moments, senior leaders must remain steadfast in their beliefs and resist buckling under this pressure.

Other times, an organization may have too much work-in-process. Two tools help with this situation. One is a method where leadership teams identify criteria, then use those criteria to filter initiatives into four relative priorities: mission critical (top priority for resources), important (done as resources are available), wait list (waiting for capacity to be freed up), and on hold (deferred for now). Senior leadership teams should identify the criteria that will be used to place the initiatives into the proper category, then to do the sorting. I have found that the method used by Catalysis and the Institute for Enterprise Excellence is very effective for facilitating teams through this decision process.

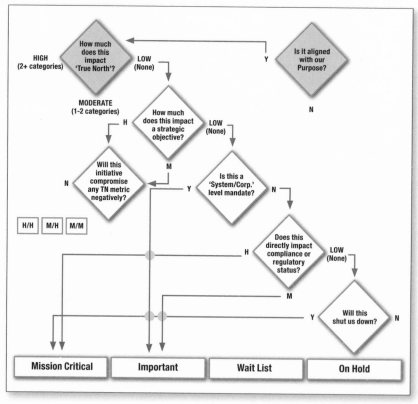

Figure 8.5. Prioritization and De-selection
Source: Institute for Enterprise Excellence

Another approach is the Drucker Institute's planned abandonment method. Famed management consultant Peter Drucker stressed in many books that the first step in strategic thinking and planning starts with getting rid of yesterday. Drucker asked the following about old products or services:

1. Are they still viable?

2. Are they likely to remain viable?

3. Do they still give value to the customer?

4. Are they likely to do so tomorrow?

5. Do they still fit the realities of population and markets, of technology and economy?

6. If not, how can you best abandon them or at least stop pouring in further resources and efforts?

Senior teams must realize that the strategic process needs to be kept constantly alive by refreshing the market position assessment, engaging others in identifying key strategic issues, and solving for those issues. This must be done continuously, not every three to five years. As described earlier, at ThedaCare we would formally collect insights from throughout the entire organization from January through March and produce a written market position assessment. Next, we would engage many stakeholders in meaningful discussions about the implications of the market position assessment, generate strategic alternatives in April and May, and then present our findings and recommendations to the board in June. Strategic imperatives would flow from that discussion and be codified into a written document. This was in addition to the daily practice of the senior leadership team going to the workplace to gain insights from frontline caregivers, weekly discussions about strategic issues and options, monthly strategy deployment reviews where we learned the results of patient-centered experiments, and every board meeting where we explored critical uncertainties.

The capacity for change develops only by repetitive practice through the application and improvement of a system for managing strategy. This is hard work for the senior leadership team. In the next chapter, I describe some challenges leaders face and suggest ways to deal with them.

Chapter 9

A Subset
of a Larger System

*I never really understood lean thinking until I had
to adopt standard work.*

—Kathryn Correia
Chief Administrative Officer
Fairview Health

The strategic management system described in the first eight chapters of this book is part of a larger lean management system. This lean management system has been documented in Kim Barnas's book *Beyond Heroes*. Many health systems throughout the world have experimented with lean management, and early returns are encouraging. The underpinning of any lean management system is the set of principles that were identified by Toyota sensei Shigeo Shingo. His writings have been formulated by the leaders at the Institute for Enterprise Excellence (IEX), which is an educational affiliate of the Shingo Institute, a leading source of lean thinking. I have learned the importance of approaching lean transformation from the perspective of principles first, then behaviors, followed by systems. I initially learned that lean is all about tools. The tools are important but are not enough to create sustained improvement. Lean is a social technical system. That means it's about both process and people.

The abbreviation for the IEX approach is:

- P=Principles
- S=Systems
- T=Tools
- R=Results

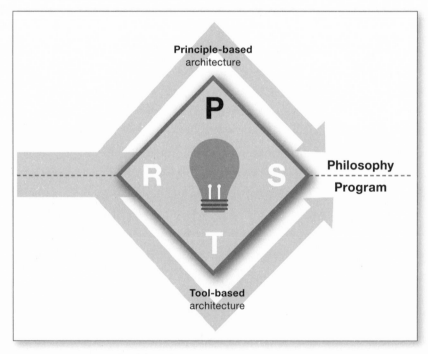

Figure 9.1. Applying the Shingo Model
Source: Institute for Enterprise Excellence, 2016

Without the bedrock of principles, behaviors, and systems, the culture of the organization does not learn to embrace PDSA thinking. Many of you may have started your lean journey with an introduction to tools such as value stream mapping, rapid improvement events, visual tracking boards, X-matrices, etc. This approach was based on the idea that adult learning required an immersion into experiential learning, that is, learning by doing. I think this may be because external consultants introduce a lot of lean tools. It's relatively easy to get a team of people engaged in learning lean tools. And the fact is using tools can achieve great results. Organizations that have viewed lean thinking as a *program*, which is strictly tool based, have found that the approach causes resentment, disengagement, and pushback.

We experienced all three at ThedaCare. Lean was introduced in 2003. By 2006, pushback from clinicians, staff, and other stakeholders was so intense that our senior leadership team launched full-day sessions to discuss why lean was a management system *philosophy*, not a program. Unfortunately, we hadn't learned at that point that the management system was based on a foundation of principles, behaviors, and systems. So, such talks mattered little. But the tools do get results, and when there were significant improvements in clinical services—such as door-to-balloon time in the case of heart attacks or success in treating depression in our behavioral health units—staff and clinicians took notice.

In retrospect, we should have anchored that work in the why. The principles are the why behind everything in the lean transformation. There are three categories of principles, each of which results in new behaviors when the principles related to that category are adhered to. Systems bring these principles and behaviors to life.

The *alignment* principles are: create constancy of purpose, create value for the patient, and think systemically. At ThedaCare, we developed systems based on the alignment principles. We created a strategic planning system tied to our system of financial forecasting that had replaced the old budgeting system. Forecasting is a process to look forward, rather than backward, at finance. It's based on the financial performance of the previous four quarters with a look forward over the next four to six quarters. In this way, operations work is adjusted quickly in order to meet financial targets, rather than waiting until the end of the budget year to realize you didn't meet your budget. John Toussaint, in his book *Management on the Mend*, devoted an entire chapter to forecasting (chapter 8). These two systems helped to align everyone in the organization around the handful of patient-centered strategies that were designed to achieve the True North metrics.

The *enable* principles include: respect every individual, lead with humility, and learn continuously. Some of these principles were embedded in the human development system, the purpose of which was to develop our people. Finally, the *improve* principles include: set a scientific method for problem solving; seek perfection; assure quality at the source; focus on process, flow, and pull value; and reduce variation. Although we fumbled a bit trying to understand all the principles, we did end up creating the ThedaCare Improvement System.

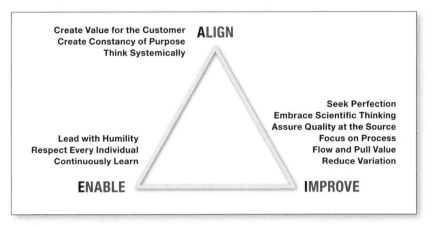

Create Value for the Customer **ALIGN**
Create Constancy of Purpose
Think Systemically

Seek Perfection
Embrace Scientific Thinking
Assure Quality at the Source
Lead with Humility | Focus on Process
Respect Every Individual | Flow and Pull Value
Continuously Learn | Reduce Variation

ENABLE | **IMPROVE**

Figure 9.2. Groups of Principles
Source: Institute for Enterprise Excellence, 2016

ThedaCare did not define the behaviors that leaders were going to hold each other accountable for. In retrospect, this was another gap in the ThedaCare Improvement System. This gap has led to a lack of sustainment of the improvement system as originally designed over time.

There are good examples where behaviors have become part of the leadership DNA. Leader behaviors have been clearly defined by Zuckerberg San Francisco General Hospitals' leadership. The behaviors include going to see the frontline work and asking open-ended questions to learn. These behaviors are anchored in the principle of respecting every individual. Using PDSA thinking is another expectation. Susan Ehrlich, the CEO, has created standard work for her calendar, which is displayed on a large whiteboard in her office that everyone sees when they visit her. She also has posted on her office door an A3. On a single sheet of paper she explains how she is doing at asking open questions and using PDSA thinking and how many times a week she is going to the gemba. ("Gemba" is a Japanese word meaning "going to where value is created.") When these core behaviors become an expectation for every leader, the culture changes. Patient-centered improvement is the result.

A strategic management system is a *subsystem* of the overall lean management system intended to provide alignment up and down the organization. The system defines what's important in order to deliver better patient-centered value. True North metrics and patient-centered strategy are examples of outputs of this system. This system has tools like those described in previous chapters. These tools, however, will not create sustainable results outside of the context of the system, and the system will not create sustainable results if senior leaders do not model the principles and behaviors.

This is why PDSA thinking is so critical to successful strategy deployment. As Catalysis executive coach Margie Hagene says, senior leaders must continually develop a "PDSA muscle" so they can model lean thinking during catch-ball. In order to create a learning organization that learns more rapidly than its competitors, everyone at all levels must become expert with lean, starting with the senior leadership team. Margie suggests that the quality of catch-ball during the strategy deployment process will be proportional to the quality of catch-ball learned by senior leaders and practiced with each other and with their direct reports.

This strategic management system connects directly to the other systems that buttress your lean transformation.

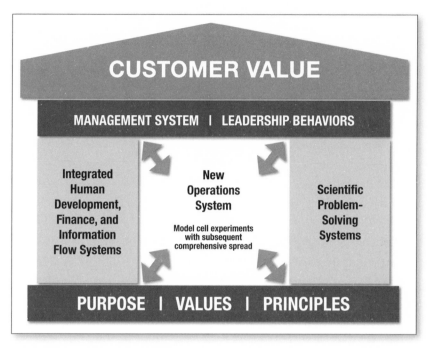

Figure 9.3. Transformation House

In this depiction from John Toussaint's book *Management on the Mend*, all of the aspects of a lean transformation "house" for healthcare are covered. The floor of the house includes defining the purpose of the organization. True North metrics and the handful of breakthrough strategies fit here. Values are the belief system by which people treat one another. Principles are the universal truths that govern the operations of the organization. In the center of the house is a new operating system called a model cell. The knowledge for the development of this new operating system comes from the rapid lean learning loops described in the patient-centered strategy system. The pillars include the scientific problem-solving system usually taught by the central improvement office and an integrated human development, finance, and information technology system that supports and improves the new operating system. Finally, the management system, which includes the strategic management system we have outlined previously, is the glue that holds the lean transformation together. Leaders' behaviors, depicted next to the management system at the roof of the house, sustain the transformation.

Maryjeanne Schaffmeyer, former chief operating officer for Appleton Medical Center and Theda Clark Medical Center at ThedaCare, describes the connection between the strategic management system and the daily improvement system. In what she calls the Ideal State Information Flow, senior leadership's strategic intent is translated to the front lines through catch-ball; in turn, a problem or opportunity comes back to the senior leadership team from the front lines. The diagram below shows strategic intent flowing from senior leadership through the organization to the frontline caregivers (Level 1). Standard work at each level helps translate strategic intent, while regularly scheduled "huddles" unearth problems for employees to solve at that level. Whenever they cannot do that, they push the problem to the next level.

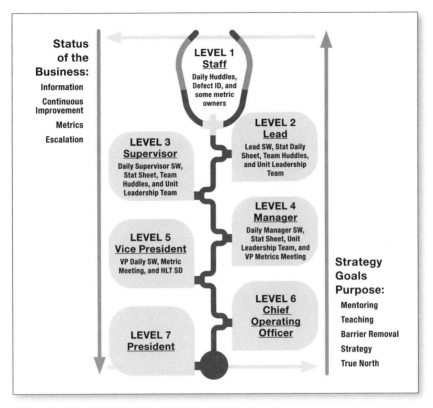

Figure 9.4. Ideal State Information Flow

When Maryjeanne teaches the Daily Management System, she uses a case study based on the ThedaCare senior leadership team's intent to improve our market position in cardiovascular services. The team used process redesign to create differentiation, as well as add a new cardiovascular surgeon. All levels at ThedaCare tried to anticipate the impact on their operations and adjust for it.

The new surgeon was more successful than we anticipated—he generated a larger number of surgeries than projected. The front line felt the impact first. Part of the postsurgical protocol was for an open-heart surgery patient to be admitted to the intensive care unit at Appleton Medical Center. During their daily huddles, the lead nurse and supervisor would review the tracking center and statistics sheet and ask the staff: "What is your biggest concern today?" Increasingly, they said the unit was filled beyond capacity and could handle no more patients. Whenever this would happen, the lead and supervisor did what they could do at that level: close the unit to new patients.

At the next level huddle, the ICU manager asked the supervisor the same question: "What is your biggest concern today?" More and more frequently, the answer came back: "We keep having to close the unit to new patients because we are full." The problem was thus escalated to the unit manager. The ICU manager, in turn, tried to solve the problem by working with physicians to improve throughput—in this case, the number of patients passing through a system—to make sure they were being discharged in an appropriate and timely manner. This solved the problem for a while, but the surgeon continued to be in demand, so the unit filled to capacity again.

As this problem increased in frequency, the ICU manager and surgical manager collaborated with the hospital's surgeons to level load the volume by spreading out surgeries over seven days rather than just five. Once again, this worked briefly, but the program's success eventually breeched the ICU's capacity. This Sisyphus-like problem needed to be escalated to the next level.

The ICU manager and the surgery manager joined forces with their vice president and developed a new step-down unit for cardiac surgery patients, staffed by ICU nurses when needed. In the short run, this reduced the stress on the ICU in times of overcapacity. Eventually, however, the Appleton Medical Center leaders determined that more intensive care beds were the solution. The hospital leadership team worked with the leadership of the system-wide cardiovascular services program to create a proposed solution for additional ICU beds and escalated it to the senior leadership team. Since ThedaCare had developed a more flexible capital allocation process, the decision to add more beds was made in a timely manner and based on patient need as identified by the people doing the work.

Maryjeanne told me that when the frontline staff discovered they could impact decisions that affected them, that increased their engagement in the ThedaCare Improvement System. In this case, the senior leadership team deployed its strategic intent by adding the cardiovascular surgeon. The new surgeon was more successful than expected, and it led to unanticipated consequences. At each level in the organization, they tried to solve the situation to the degree they had the ability, and at each level they had some success in solving it. When the solution required a decision at a higher level, they were able to escalate the situation to that level.

Success at lean management is about leadership and leader behaviors. I had to learn this the hard way. Early in my career I was assigned the implementation of a Management by Objectives program at my organization. Management by Objectives was first described by Peter Drucker in his 1954 book *The Practice of Management*. Subsequently, practitioners refined his thoughts into systems and tools, which I followed to complete my task. Unfortunately, I found that other senior leaders interpreted Drucker's approach as "get me the results and I don't care how you do it." While Drucker never expected his concepts to be taken to this extreme, that is what happened in many organizations and continues to happen even today. When management is practiced this way, short-term improvements may occur. Eventually, however, they will be unsustainable because no method or process exists to continue to produce those results.

This is why it was so hard for me to learn my new mental model of an organization as a social system and a leader as a people developer and coach. Rather than issuing orders and telling people what to do or issuing orders and causing subordinates to follow them regardless of consequences, I had to learn to give them a job and let them try to accomplish it. I needed to communicate what the target was and why it was important. I also had to help them develop sustainable, repetitive process improvement to keep hitting that target without creating collateral damage in other parts of the organization. Then I needed to coach them at the place where they were creating value through study and adjust rapid learning loops.

One of the most articulate advocates of how to be an effective CEO in the twenty-first century and how to use lean is Eric Dickson, MD, president and CEO of the University of Massachusetts Memorial Health Care (UMMHC).

UMMHC is the largest healthcare system in central and western Massachusetts and was formed in 1998 through the merger of Memorial Hospital with the clinical system of the University of Massachusetts. It consists of UMass Memorial Medical Center, a level 1 trauma center and the major teaching hospital of UMass Medical School, as well as three community hospitals and a number of ambulatory clinics throughout central Massachusetts. The organization has more than 1,200 active medical staff and 2,200 registered nurses active in over 22 communities. They also offer emergency services such as LifeFlight, long-term care facilities, home health and rehabilitation, and behavioral health services. UMMHC has been ranked as the number one hospital in New England for surviving and treating a heart attack for many years. In 2008, the hospital ranked second in the United States for heart attack survival.

UMMHC faced a downhill financial slide, leading to a $55-million operating loss in fiscal 2013. The organization was criticized for being inefficient and wasteful in the press and by state legislators. In addition, changes in healthcare reimbursement impacted the medical center severely. In response to this criticism and these challenges, UMMHC underwent significant restructuring toward a leaner business model.

Eric was chosen to turn UMMHC around. Prior to this, he was involved in lean efforts for a decade at UMMHC. Now in charge of 13,000 people, he says his primary task is to change all employees from problem identifiers to problem solvers so as to foster greater frontline caregiving to patients.

This is a major personal challenge. He began as an emergency doctor and a supervisor of a trauma center. By experience and training he was used to taking over in an environment of total chaos by telling people what to do. When he became CEO, Eric had to learn how to listen, but he admits he has had a hard time doing this on a consistent basis. Eric can assume control over a meeting without being aware of it. He now asks his colleagues and staff to tell him when he engages in such behavior. When they do, he thanks them.

In order to manage the front lines most effectively, Eric believes he has to create a cascade of goals and a catch-ball process so that the customer experience improves dramatically from the door to the floor. As a manager he has to learn how to help employees by creating dialogue so that the flow of ideas can flow downward and upward. As a CEO he has to personally get closer to the work they experience.

Eric thinks that as a CEO he doesn't run anything. Rather, his job is to conduct meetings on a regular basis and keep moving the strategy along by asking questions such as: Why is there a gap between our strategy and our performance? Why are we not closing the gap? Why are we not achieving a 20% improvement?

What he asks of himself is: How can I help the good people who are working very hard? What is needed? Where are people having troubles? How do I get as many of the 13,000 employees involved in strategy? How many daily, weekly, monthly can I enroll?

Eric admits that he constantly engages in lean practices. The senior leadership team sets goals and deadlines. They ask: Where are we today? Why are there gaps? How do we track improvement? They then report to a team of 15 every quarter to ask: Is this still the right project? Is it completed, or does it need to be modified?

Says Eric, "At UMMHC we have 10 True North metrics, and we put them on the wall so we can see who owns these, why a gap exists, and how well we are managing these projects. We constantly have to monitor the measures, the budget, and the targets."

When this management system works well, it makes problems and opportunities visible and engages professionals in solving them. It creates dialogue around the nature of the problem to be solved and recognizes that any proposed solution is a hypothesis that must be tested through rapid experimentation. It reduces the number of arguments about who is right by letting the process determine what is right. The ultimate solution is likely to be something created together, rather than a result of one person's intuition.

Sustaining momentum requires a senior leadership team to model PDSA behavior, make the problems and opportunities visible, display the work required to solve them, and choose which ones to tackle first while deferring other items until capacity is available. The decisions should always be informed from what is being learned at the front line about customer needs. The broader lean management system, which includes constant dialogue using catch-ball, regular huddles, and escalation if necessary, is critical. The leadership team must put the real problems on the table and discuss them. No one should be allowed to subvert the process. The team must take the responsibility for choosing and deferring. And they must support each other when explaining priorities to those disappointed that their ideas have been deferred, at least temporarily.

PDSA thinking must be applied at every level in the organization. Clinicians must use PDSA to manage individual patients. Unit managers must use PDSA to solve daily improvement opportunities. Senior leaders must use PDSA to make choices and engage others in deployment.

When I retired from ThedaCare, Jim Matheson, my vice president of marketing, became the senior vice president and assumed responsibility for the strategic planning value stream. He and the ThedaCare team have made huge strides in capturing the insights gained at the service line level and incorporating them into the enterprise-wide strategic planning process.

Imagine if all of your service lines and operating units conducted their business in the manner described above and fed what they learned to each other and to the senior leadership team in an organized, methodical manner. You will have created a lean management system with a strategic management subsystem that is focused on patient-centered performance and is achieving world-class results. You are on your way to creating a learning organization! Now let's review everything you have learned.

Chapter 10

The Journey Ahead

A journey of a thousand miles begins with a single step.

—Lao Tzu

I n this book, I have laid out the details of my journey to understand lean and how it applies to a healthcare strategic management system. I made that first step after my performance review with John Toussaint. You took your first step when you picked up this book. Let's see how far you have come in only a few chapters.

In the first section, I laid out a framework to increase velocity and success in strategic planning, execution, and alignment. This framework synthesizes and simplifies the concepts of current thought leaders on strategic planning.

Specifically, in chapter 1, I explained that my old way of thinking about strategic planning was based on a command-and-control mental model. My personal awakening started when I realized that my role was not to be a strategic planning hero, diagnosing and solving the organization's issues; rather, my role was to build the capability in the organization to practice strategic thinking. This capability requires a system with tools for formulating, executing, and monitoring strategy. The foundation for this system is plan-do-study-adjust thinking. PDSA thinking is the common language that unites senior leaders and clinicians in patient-centered value creation. When we work together using PDSA thinking, we stop arguing about who is right because we may all be right. We run experiments to test hypotheses and let the patients decide what is right for them.

Chapter 2 focused on putting strategy back into strategy deployment. I argued for the need to achieve differentiation through process redesign rather than asset acquisition. I then explained that achieving your ideal state requires senior leaders to make choices of strategic initiatives that will produce unique, differentiating value while reserving capacity for other big-rock projects that must be done to stay in business. And I delineated how PDSA can help with such problems using specific examples from my own experiences and those of several healthcare organizations.

The next section provides a process for applying the framework of strategic planning, execution, and alignment through a repeatable method. Woven throughout these chapters were examples of early successes with this framework.

In chapter 3, I urged you to realize the complexity of the situation that you are in—the mess—before you design your business model. In such a world, CEOs and senior leaders must work together to create a shared understanding of their reality, a vision of what great looks like, and a plan to obtain such a state. I then outlined a number of strategic management tools that can enable this shared understanding and illustrated with examples. I discussed how you can capture the essentials of your transactional environment and explore the context of your industry, and I delineated a number of ways for you to analyze the forces that impact your organization so you and your leadership can achieve a shared vision of an ideal state. Most important, start from need; deeply understand your customers' pain points so you can discover ways to provide unique, relevant value to them. These insights are most often captured by frontline caregivers.

Framing the strategic issue was the topic for chapter 4. The lean strategic management system is built on PDSA and is derived by framing your organization's strategic issue—the compelling problem or opportunity you face. I propose a process to begin this inquiry that includes determining your current state, your ideal state, and your target state and the gap between them. Such discussions lead inevitably to the question of when innovation is required—what Ted Toussaint defined as an environment where "people use new knowledge and understanding to experiment with new possibilities in order to implement new concepts that create new value."

Chapter 5 emphasized the need to make strategic choices, aided by specific tools. Each choice that you make is a hypothesis, based on assumptions you are making about your own capabilities and the behaviors of others. I've learned that Matthew May's adaptation of Lafley and Martin's Playing to Win approach helps teams generate meaningful, well-defined, hypothetical, strategic options for the problem or opportunity you are trying to solve.

The next chapter's theme was strategy deployment through rapid experimentation. In chapter 6, I asked you the question: What must be true—regarding your customers, your competitors, and your ability to execute your strategy? I defined strategy deployment as the process of rapid experimentation to prove whether your hypothesis is true or false. This is done through a succession of lean learning loops to build out a solution by testing critical, unknown assumptions in a disciplined, methodical manner. I illustrated this process using examples from ThedaCare and Atrius Health, among other organizations.

In chapter 7, I described the power of catch-ball, both its technical and human sides. Catch-ball is a continuous, ongoing process of identifying priorities, making decisions, discussing implications, and reallocating resources. On the technical side, I introduced the X-matrix as a method of enabling dialogue between people and as a way to implement strategic intent. On the human dimension, I discussed the need for respect, dialogue, and the ability to negotiate throughout all levels of an organization. I presented a model of how to engage in critical conversations and drew on lessons from my son Jesse who is a Marine. Finally, I described a template to practice and improve catch-ball.

In chapter 8, I discussed the visual management systems and senior leadership processes with which the senior leadership team studies the work-in-process and keeps emerging ideas from leaping into top-priority status without being vetted through an evaluation system. This cements the strategic management system as an iterative process of adaptive learning, a shared leadership competency.

In chapter 9, I briefly reviewed the entirety of the lean management system and how the strategic management system fits as a subsystem into lean management. I explained the underlying principles of lean management and the behaviors that must logically emanate from those principles. I used the specific example of how a new cardiac surgeon at ThedaCare tested the strategic management system and how that system led to senior management making important decisions that improved the patient and caregiver experiences.

So what are your next steps? I had to start with questioning my own mental models and behaviors. I had to explore what it was like to leave my office behind and go to where people were creating value for patients, and I had to figure out what my role in that was. I had to appreciate the role of shared visual management systems and leader standard work so that I had a basis upon which to improve my ability to create value for patients and for the organization. I had to learn how to develop the capability in my direct reports to solve complex issues, rather than solving them for them. I had to acquire new skills in design thinking and innovation, beginning with the process in which frontline caregivers could uncover deep customer insights. I had to devote myself to getting better at PDSA thinking and how to coach others.

There are many challenges to changing mental models and the strategic planning systems that result from them:

- The complexity of the situation. Senior executives feel the enormous effects of a transforming industry and feel less and less in control over the situation.

- It's very hard to align the key participants in any complex organization around a common brand promise. As my friend and leading brand consultant Karl Speak says, everyone in the organization is asking themselves this question: "If I help the organization become more of what it wants to be, do I get to become more of who I want to be?" The very nature of healthcare organizations as professional bureaucracies makes it even harder.

- Making choices can offend some key stakeholders. No one wants to be viewed as secondary; everyone wants to see himself or herself front and center in the strategic plan. Unfortunately, this can lead back to creating broad categorical labels of activity that can leave room for any project that professionals believe is important, resulting in overburden and lack of focus.

- Your existing financial mechanisms are not designed to support rapid experimentation and lean learning loops. The budget mentality reinforces the mental model of predict and predetermine. Innovation and rapid experimentation require a new way to think about measuring progress.

Despite these obstacles, there are best practices for proceeding. I recommend starting this strategic management system with one aspect of your business where you know you have a key strategic issue that must be solved. It could be a service line where you have a significant problem or opportunity. It could be a channel strategy such as developing a new customer-based primary care proposition or determining your position in the insurance market. Choose a model cell, and apply this strategic management system to gain knowledge and confidence. Remember that the model cell is an inch wide and mile deep. It should result in radical process redesign to achieve breakthrough performance.

ThedaCare started with two model cells: patients suffering from breast cancer and the most chronically frail of ThedaCare Physicians' patients in two of their 23 sites. North Memorial started experimenting with a new value proposition for a target audience in one of its many clinics. The Ashland and Hayward hospitals began experiments to move from transactional to deeper long-term customer relationships in model cells. Catalysis launched with a minimum viable product and built out its transformation approach using senior executives in a handful of dedicated organizations. This strategic management system is scalable to larger organizations. Lafley and Martin proved that with Proctor & Gamble. The lesson to learn: start an inch wide and a mile deep.

As you begin to model the principles and behaviors of this new strategic management system and foster innovation through rapid learning cycles, you need to protect your model cells from the inevitable reaction of stakeholders from the existing business model who want to kill off the innovation effort. Their behavior is not intentional, but it is inevitable. The more disruptive the innovation is to the existing business model, the greater the risk is to these stakeholders. We frequently experienced this reaction when our ThedaCare at Work employer solutions group would develop new value propositions that would threaten the business model of ThedaCare Physicians. The first reaction of ThedaCare Physicians was usually to restrict the spread of the innovation. This reaction is normal. You must facilitate catch-ball alignment discussions to counter it. If you leave transformation to chance, your innovation efforts will be stifled.

That's a lot of information to absorb and a lot of work to undertake. The complexity of the industry, the unique nature of healthcare organizations, and the change management challenge of rallying autonomous professionals around a common brand promise may seem daunting. But if I have learned anything from lean thinking, it is that removing waste from the process creates the space and time to address the unique, difficult work that requires your best effort. While the issues are complex and difficult, the system of strategic management does not have to be. When you put the strategic options on the table and use visual management and standard work to process those ideas in a way that you can learn rapidly, your patients and everyone in the organization wins.

My hope is that now that you have finished the book, you will have learned the full value of lean thinking in strategic planning and can use it to transform your organizations to the highest level of performance possible to best serve your patients. In short, you are on your way to creating a patient-centered strategy.

I am still partway on my journey. I'm excited to continue this journey because it leads to better healthcare for my family, my friends, and my community, which is why I initially chose to work in this field. I have learned much over the years, and I invite you to join me on this quest. There is much I need to learn from you. This will have enormous benefits for you and for everyone in your organization who seeks the joyful experience that Dr. Kevin Croston suggested was the true goal of medicine.

Acknowledgments

To the many giants who have allowed me to stand on their shoulders and look for a better way. I especially want to thank Matthew E. May for his guidance and patience over the past few years. If not for him, I would not have ventured into new territory and seen with open eyes. John Shook provides a continuous beacon to keep me from getting lost.

There are so many contributors to this thinking who have given me guidance and willingly contributed their knowledge and expertise. Many of them are fellow faculty members at Catalysis. All are fellow lifelong students who want to make things better for others. At the risk of my forgetting someone, they include Katie Anderson, Kim Barnas, Kathryn Correia, Patsy Engel, Kathy Franklin, Matt Furlan, Roger Gerard, Mark Graban, Margie Hagene, Tom Hartman, Karl Hoover, Marta Karlov, Bill Katz, David Krebs, Pat Mages, Theresa Moore, Steve Player, John Poole, Jake Raymer, Michael Sachs, Maryjeanne Schaffmeyer, Sharon Schumacher, Karl Speak, Mike Speer, Mike Stoecklein, Kent Thompson, Ted Toussaint, Brian Veara, Tom Wiltzius, and Helen Zak.

I have been so fortunate over my career to have reported to CEOs and senior leaders who took a sincere interest in my development as a person and as an executive. They saw something in me that I sometimes didn't see in myself and encouraged me to stay enrolled in the School of Hard Knocks. They include Roy Wheatley, Gary Stay, John Howard, John Casey, Errol Biggs, Ed French, Steve Taylor, Jim Raney, John Toussaint, and Dean Gruner.

I am grateful to the pioneer executives who have left the old way behind and have been willing to experiment with this system, making it better: Kevin Croston, MD, Tiffany Zitzewitz, Eric Dickson, MD, Jason Douglas, Tim Gillingsrud, Kevin Stranberg, Cherie Morgan, Luke Bierl, Michael Frohna, Jon Goreham, Fred Young, Jerome Martin, Lance Crane, and Keith Livingston.

Later in my career I was fortunate to have colleagues who taught me what it really meant to develop people to improve process and serve purpose. They include Michael Frohna, Julie Imig, Jim Matheson, Paula Morgen, and Joe Van Dehy. I wish I had learned this earlier; the list could have been much longer.

I was blessed that Larry Rothstein joined me in the writing of this book. He could have pivoted, but he persevered with me through the many iterations it took to make this a story worth telling.

John Toussaint and Jim Womack provided continual inspiration and clarity of purpose. Many times along the way, they pulled me out of a ditch and set me back on the road with greater vision about what was important. John provided the red pen that would get us un-stuck and keep us aligned with the target audience, and Devon Ritter kept a steady eye on the details.

My friends at Catalysis did all the heavy lifting to get this from conception to the finish line. I'm especially grateful to Steve Bollinger, Rachel Regan, and Sara Thompson for their dedication to this project.

My loving wife, Deborah, offered critical thinking and continued encouragement and allowed me to shirk all my household responsibilities for the past year while I tried to capture my learning in this book. She also gave me honest advice from a lean leader's point of view. Our children, Jesse, Stephanie, Royce, and Abigail, have continually contributed by asking great questions and providing sage advice.

References and Further Reading

Balle, Michael, Daniel Jones, Jacques Chaize, and Orest Fiume. *The Lean Strategy: Using Lean to Create Competitive Advantage, Unleash Innovation, and Deliver Sustainable Growth.* New York: McGraw-Hill Education, 2017.

Barnas, Kim. *Beyond Heroes: A Lean Management System for Healthcare.* Appleton, WI: Catalysis, 2014.

Blank, Steve. *The Four Steps to the Epiphany: Successful Strategies for Products That Win.* Somerset, TX: K&S Ranch, 2013.

Brown, Tim. *Change by Design: How Design Thinking Transforms Organizations and Inspires Innovation.* New York: Harper-Collins, 2009.

De Geus, Arie. "Planning as Learning." *Harvard Business Review*, March 1988.

Drucker, Peter F. *The Practice of Management.* New York: Harper-Collins, 1954.

Fick, Nathaniel. *One Bullet Away: The Making of a Marine Officer.* Boston: Houghton Mifflin, 2005.

Gharajedaghi, Jamshid. *Systems Thinking: Managing Chaos and Complexity.* 3rd ed. Burlington, MA: Morgan Kaufmann, 2011.

Graban, Mark. *Lean Hospitals: Improving Quality, Patient Safety, and Employee Engagement.* 3rd ed. New York: Productivity Press, 2016.

Institute for Enterprise Excellence. "One Approach to Deploying a Purpose and Principle-Driven Transformation." April 2016. http://bit.ly/IEXdeploy4.

Isaacs, William. *Dialogue and the Art of Thinking Together.* New York: Doubleday, 1999.

Jackson, Thomas L. *Hoshin Kanri for the Lean Enterprise: Developing Competitive Capabilities and Managing Profit.* New York: Productivity Press, 2006.

Lafley, A. G., and Roger L. Martin. *Playing to Win: How Strategy Really Works.* Boston: Harvard Business Review, 2013.

Lafley, A.G., Roger Martin, and Jennifer Riel. "A Playbook for Strategy: The Five Essential Questions at the Heart of Any Winning Strategy." *Rotman Management Magazine,* Winter 2013.

May, Matthew E. *The Elegant Solution: Toyota's Formula for Mastering Innovation.* New York: Free Press, 2007.

May, Matthew E. *Winning the Brain Game: Fixing the 7 Fatal Flaws of Thinking.* New York: McGraw-Hill, 2016.

McNally, David, and Karl D. Speak. *Be Your Own Brand.* 2nd ed. San Francisco: Berrett-Koehler, 2011.

Mintzburg, Henry. *The Rise and Fall of Strategic Planning.* New York: Free Press, 1994.

Patterson, Kerry, Joseph Grenny, Ron McMillan, and Al Switzler. *Crucial Conversations: Tools for Talking When Stakes Are High.* New York: McGraw-Hill, 2002.

Porter, Michael E. "What Is Strategy?" *Harvard Business Review*, November–December 1996.

Ries, Eric. *The Lean Startup: How Today's Entrepreneurs Use Continuous Innovation to Create Radically Successful Businesses.* New York: Crown, 2011.

Rother, Mike, and John Shook. *Learning to See: Value Stream Mapping to Add Value and Eliminate Muda.* Brookline, MA: Lean Enterprise Institute, 1998.

Schein, Edgar H. *Humble Inquiry: The Gentle Art of Asking Instead of Telling.* San Francisco: Berrett-Koehler, 2013.

Senge, Peter M. *The Fifth Discipline: The Art and Practice of the Learning Organization.* Revised. New York: Doubleday, 2006.

Stanfield, R. Brian, ed. *The Art of Focused Conversation: 100 Ways to Access Group Wisdom in the Workplace.* Gabriola Island, BC, Canada: New Society, 2000.

Team FME. *PESTLE Analysis: Strategy Skills.* Available at http://www.free-management-ebooks.com/dldebk-pdf/fme-pestle-analysis.pdf.

Team FME. *Porter's Five Forces: Strategy Skills.* Available at http://www.free-management-ebooks.com/dldebk-pdf/fme-five-forces-framework.pdf.

Toussaint, John, MD. *Management on the Mend: The Healthcare Executive Guide to System Transformation.* Appleton, WI: Catalysis, 2015.

Toussaint, Ted, Karen DaSilva, and John S. Toussaint. "How Atrius Health Is Making the Shift from Volume to Value." *Harvard Business Review,* December 13, 2016.

Endnote

This book is published by Catalysis, an organization established to transform the healthcare industry into a safer, lower-cost system that provides better value for patients. Catalysis was formed in 2008 by the Board of Trustees of ThedaCare Inc. to offer education, coaching, and networking opportunities.

Using the knowledge from the highest-performing healthcare organization around the world, Catalysis is constantly expanding its curriculum of educational materials, experiential learning opportunities, and peer-to-peer collaborative learning networks. Many of these resources are free. This book is just one offering for organizations seeking to align leadership behaviors with lean thinking. For additional information, please visit createvalue.org.

In addition to our resources, Catalysis also holds events all around the world, including our annual Lean Healthcare Transformation Summit in the United States and Europe. We have expanded our educational workshops to dozens of popular subjects like Kata in Healthcare, Lean Management Systems, and Building Enterprise Excellence. And if you would like to have us bring the training to you, Catalysis now offers customized live and virtual education. For more information visit createvalue.org/workshops.

Your opportunity to network with the best healthcare leaders in the world can be realized by joining the Catalysis Healthcare Value Network. This collection of organizations is at the forefront of understanding what it takes to truly transform healthcare. For more information visit createvalue.org/networks/healthcare-value-network.

Index

Note: Page numbers in *italics* indicate figures.